LITTLE RED
RIDING
HOOD

Retold by Moira Andrew

Illustrated by Cliff Wright

Once upon a time there was a girl
called Little Red Riding Hood.
She lived with her mother and father
in a little cottage by a forest.

Every day when Little Red Riding
Hood went out to play she put on the
red cloak that her grandmother had
made for her. It had a beautiful red
hood and that is why she was called
Red Riding Hood.

One day Little Red Riding Hood's
mother said, 'Grandmother is ill.
I want you to take her a cake. But
you must stay on the path and do
not stop to talk to anyone.'

So Little Red Riding Hood put
on her red cloak and set off for her
grandmother's cottage.

Little Red Riding Hood had only gone
a little way when she met a wolf.
'Hello,' said the wolf. 'Where are you
going in your beautiful red cloak?'

The wolf looked very kind, so Little
Red Riding Hood said, 'I am going
to see my grandmother who lives in
a cottage in the forest. I am taking
her a cake because she is ill.'

'Why don't you take her some
flowers as well?' said the wolf.
'Yes, Grandmother likes flowers,'
said Little Red Riding Hood.
So she went off to get some.

But the wolf wasn't kind. He was a big bad wolf. When he saw that Little Red Riding Hood had gone to get the flowers, he ran as fast as he could to Grandmother's cottage.

When he came to Grandmother's door,
Grandmother called out, 'Who's there?'
'It's me, Little Red Riding Hood,'
said the big bad wolf. 'I have a cake
for you.'
'Come in, come in,' said Grandmother.

So the wolf opened the door and
went into the cottage.
'Oh no!' said Grandmother when she
saw the big bad wolf.
'Oh yes!' said the wolf, and he ate
her up in one go.

Then he put on
Grandmother's
nightcap and
jumped into
her bed.

Just then Little Red Riding Hood
came to the door.

'Who's there?' called the wolf.

'It's me, Little Red Riding Hood,'
she said.

'Come in, come in,' said the wolf.
So Little Red Riding Hood opened
the door and went into the cottage.

Little Red Riding Hood looked at
her grandmother.
'Grandmother, what big eyes you
have,' she said.
'All the better to see you with,'
said the big bad wolf.

Little Red Riding Hood went up
to the bed. She looked again at
her grandmother.
'Grandmother, what big ears you
have,' she said.
'All the better to hear you with,'
said the big bad wolf.

'And Grandmother, what big teeth you
have,' said Little Red Riding Hood.
'All the better to eat you with,' said
the big bad wolf.
The wolf jumped out of bed and ran
after Little Red Riding Hood.
'Help!' shouted Little Red Riding Hood
as loudly as she could. 'Help! Help!'

In the forest a woodcutter was cutting some wood. When he heard Little Red Riding Hood shouting, he ran into the cottage and hit the wolf with his axe. And that was the end of the big bad wolf.

'Thank you,' said Little Red Riding Hood. 'But what about Grandmother? The wolf has eaten her up.'

So the woodcutter took his axe,
cut open the wolf, and out jumped
Grandmother.

From that day on, Little Red Riding
Hood went to see her grandmother
every day, but never again did she
stop to talk to anyone on the way.

BRIT
MOUSE TRAPS
AND THEIR MAKERS

DAVID DRUMMOND

First published in 2008
by Mouse Trap Books
22 Knoll Road, Dorking, Surrey RH4 3EP

British Library Cataloguing in Publication Data
A catalogue record for this book is available from the British Library

ISBN: 978-0-9557923-0-4

Designed by Louise Millar

Printed by SUMMIT Print Ltd, Dorking

Contents

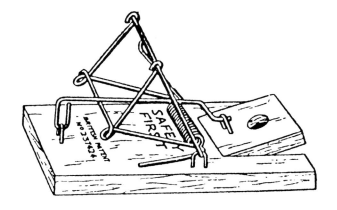

Notes on the Traps and their Illustrations

Where traps have been provided with names by their manufacturers or distributors, such names are printed in bold italics. In a few cases where a trap seems not to have been given a name, it is named after its inventor – also in bold italics.

All the illustrations are derived from digital photographs in the possession of the author. The names of owners of traps who have kindly permitted their traps to be photographed for use in this book are included in the acknowledgements. Most of the illustrations are of unset traps, but where there is a difference in appearance between a set and an unset trap, a picture of a set trap is accompanied by the word "set".

Introduction

My main purpose in writing this book is to record all known makers, by which I mean both designers and manufacturers, of mouse traps in Britain and to describe and illustrate the traps that they produced. Thus the main part of this book is concerned necessarily with the period stretching from the last half of the nineteenth century up to the present day. Before this period it is not possible to associate any particular designer or manufacturer with any particular trap. Nevertheless it will be worthwhile to introduce our topic by first taking a look, if only briefly, at the early array of mouse traps that have subsequently been replaced.

The origin of some British mouse trap designs can be traced back to pottery rodent traps in use in the Middle East in the 3rd Millenium BC[1]. But it is not until the late Middle Ages that we begin to get a clear idea of the use of mouse traps in Britain. A sixteenth century book by Leonard Mascall[2,3], Clerk of the Kitchen to the Archbishop of Canterbury, revealed that by then there were already a great variety of small traps specially designed to capture house mice. Such traps (Fig. 1) included those that could catch mice alive and also those, such as dead-falls[4] and snap traps that killed them on the spot. Some of them can even be identified as the forerunners of those in use today.

During this early period mouse traps were constructed almost entirely of wood and were undoubtedly the handiwork of local carpenters. Over the next two centuries there was a gradual improvement in trap design, with wireworkers playing a more important role, particularly by the provision of stronger and more efficient springs. At this time probably most carpenters still retained the making of mouse traps as a small part of a whole range of wooden items that they made for their local communities, but some degree of specialisation was on the way. We know for example that towards the end of the eighteenth century no less than three mouse trap makers, Mark Saunders, William Smith and Joseph

Ward were identified in Sketchley's Birmingham Directory[5]. Unfortunately no record remains of exactly what types of mouse trap each was making. However they probably included some of those surviving mouse traps that nicely fill the gap between those of Mascall's time and those that we shall deal with later. These are a deadfall trap (Fig. 2a), various single-catch live traps (Figs 2b-2d), a choker trap (Fig. 2e) and guillotine traps (Figs 2f, g and h). Apart from the deadfall that remains the same as Mascall's fall trap, they all reveal improvements on those described by Mascall. His "string and clicket" setting/release mechanisms are replaced by simpler and more durable wire arrangements and strong helical springs replace simple ones. Perhaps, however, of particular interest is the appearance of a multicatch live mouse trap with a simple internal see-saw (Figs 2i and j) that no doubt paved the way for the more complex ones that were introduced later.

Specialisation in mouse trap production by individual manufacturers undoubtedly continued throughout the nineteenth century and was helped by the great improvement in transport, especially the railways, and the subsequent springing up of wholesale and retail outlets that advertised their wares. It is only however from 1850 that we can discover the names of mouse trap makers in relation to the traps that they were making and begin to write their history. Thus this book starts with Colin Pullinger and his traps and continues up to the present day, more or less in chronological order, with the other most successful players in the field. The less successful, sometimes only represented by an entry in a catalogue, are dealt with in a further chapter. A subsequent chapter collects together a number of British mouse traps for which there seems to be no known manufacturer.

Finally in the last chapter I have recorded briefly an ever increasing number of mouse traps that are now available in Britain, but whose origin, at any rate as far as the design of their mechanism is concerned, can be ascribed to an overseas country, most often the USA. Throughout the period under review there has been a move away from wood to the use of metal and particularly, most recently, plastic. There has also been a relatively recent move to arrange for mouse traps to be manufactured in Taiwan and China.

Nearly all the mouse traps described in this book have been designed and made for the purpose of controlling house mice in domestic and commercial premises, but I have also included some very similar traps, mostly designed by academics, for the study of wild outdoor populations of other small rodents such as field mice and voles.

Fig. 1 Models of some of Mascall's Mediaeval Mouse Traps

Fig. 1a Mill to take mice

set

Fig. 1b Fall

Fig. 1c Following trappe

set

Fig. 1d Double trappe

set

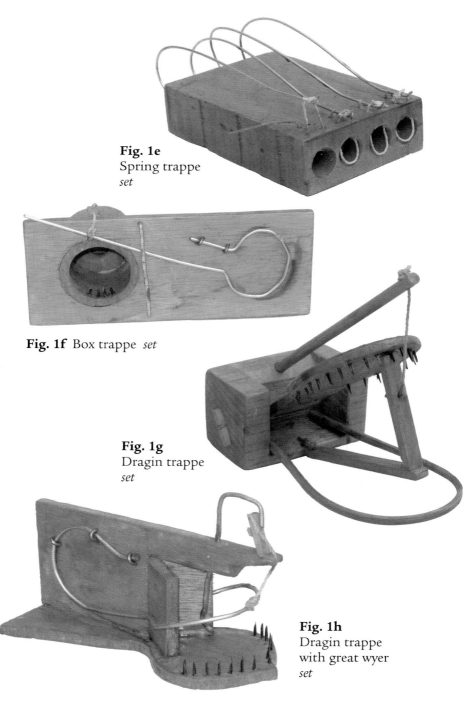

Fig. 1e
Spring trappe
set

Fig. 1f Box trappe *set*

Fig. 1g
Dragin trappe
set

Fig. 1h
Dragin trappe
with great wyer
set

9

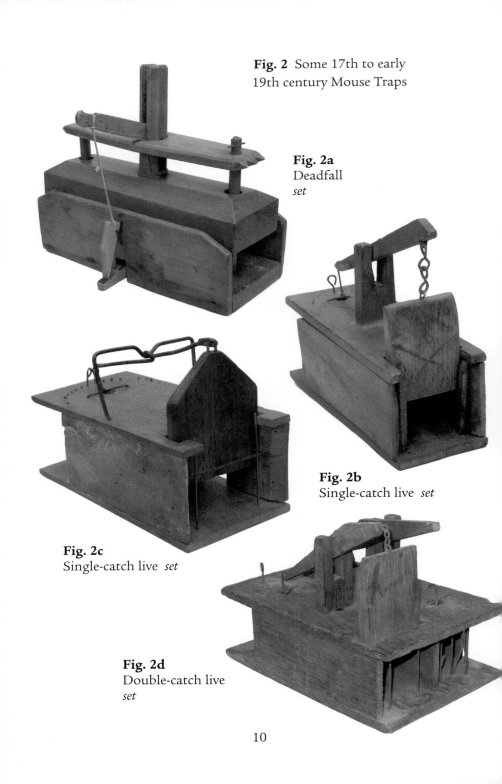

Fig. 2 Some 17th to early 19th century Mouse Traps

Fig. 2a
Deadfall
set

Fig. 2b
Single-catch live *set*

Fig. 2c
Single-catch live *set*

Fig. 2d
Double-catch live
set

10

Fig. 2e
3-hole 'Irish'
set

Fig. 2f
Double
guillotine with
single spring

Fig. 2g
Double
guillotine with
helical spring

Fig. 2h
Double guillotine
shown set

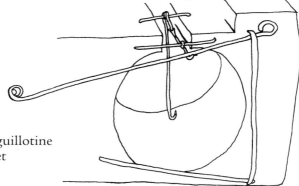

Fig. 2i
Multi-catch live box
trap with see-saw

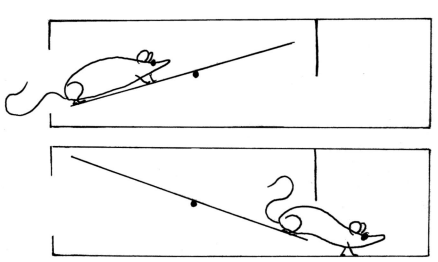

Fig. 2j
Mechanism of multi-catch live trap with see-saw

Major Manufacturers

Colin Pullinger's Inventive Factory[6] 1858 – 1920s

Colin Pullinger was born in 1814 in the village of Selsey on the coast of West Sussex. In 1847 he inherited his father's Selsey carpentry business along with his family home and associated workshops and timber-yard, as well as some six acres of adjoining farmland. It was here that he spent the rest of his life with his wife and children, and became involved with an incredible variety of activities as revealed

COLIN PULLINGER,
SELSEY, NEAR CHICHESTER,
Contractor, Inventor, Fisherman, and Mechanic,
FOLLOWING THE VARIOUS TRADES OF A
BUILDER, CARPENTER, JOINER, SAWYER, UNDERTAKER,
Turner, Cooper, Painter, Glazier, Wooden Pump Maker,
PAPER HANGER, BELL HANGER, SIGN PAINTER,
BOAT BUILDER,
CLOCK CLEANER, REPAIRER OF LOCKS, AND KEYS FITTED,
Repairer of Umbrellas and Parasols, Mender of China and Glass,
Copying Clerk, Letter Writer, Accountant, Teacher of Navigation,
GROCER, BAKER, FARMER,
Assessor and Collector of Taxes, Surveyor, House Agent, Engineer, Land Measurer, Assistant Overseer, Clerk at the Parish Vestry Meetings,
Clerk to the Selsey Police, Clerk to the Selsey Sparrow Club,
Has served at Sea in the four Quarters of the World, as Seaman, Cook, Steward, Mate and Navigator.

THE MAKER AND INVENTOR OF THE FOLLOWING:
AN IMPROVED HORSE HOE, AN IMPROVED SCARIFIER,
A newly-invented Couch Grass Rake, a Machine to Tar Ropes, Model of a Vessel to cut asunder Chains put across the Mouth of a Harbour,
A CURIOUS MOUSE TRAP,
Made on a scientific principle, where each one caught resets the trap to catch its next neighbour, requires no fresh baiting, and will catch them by dozens,
A Rat Trap on a peculiar Construction,
That will catch and put them into the trap,
An improved Mole Trap, an improved Velocipede, Model of a fast-sailing Yacht on an improved construction, 3ft. long, and challenged to sail against any Boat of the same length in the world, &c., &c., &c.

CRABS, LOBSTERS, AND PRAWNS SENT TO ANY PART OF ENGLAND.
MOUSE TRAPS LET ON HIRE.

Fig. 3 Colin Pullinger's Trade Card

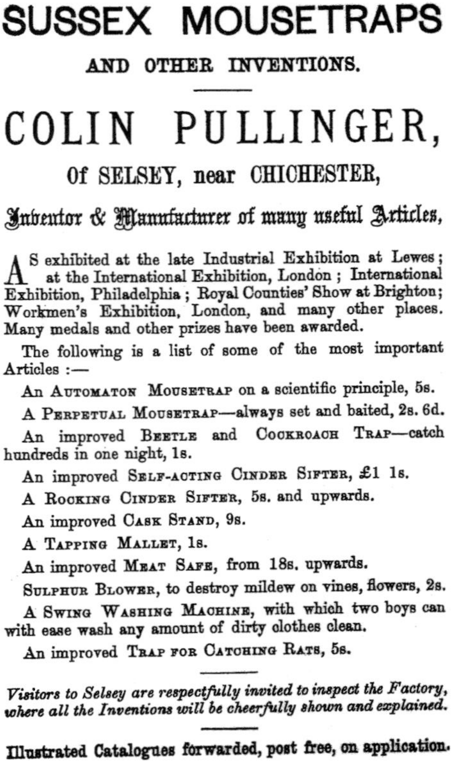

SUSSEX MOUSETRAPS

AND OTHER INVENTIONS.

COLIN PULLINGER,

Of SELSEY, near CHICHESTER,

Inventor & Manufacturer of many useful Articles,

AS exhibited at the late Industrial Exhibition at Lewes; at the International Exhibition, London; International Exhibition, Philadelphia; Royal Counties' Show at Brighton; Workmen's Exhibition, London, and many other places. Many medals and other prizes have been awarded.

The following is a list of some of the most important Articles :—

An AUTOMATON MOUSETRAP on a scientific principle, 5s.

A PERPETUAL MOUSETRAP—always set and baited, 2s. 6d.

An improved BEETLE and COCKROACH TRAP—catch hundreds in one night, 1s.

An improved SELF-ACTING CINDER SIFTER, £1 1s.

A ROCKING CINDER SIFTER, 5s. and upwards.

An improved CASK STAND, 9s.

A TAPPING MALLET, 1s.

An improved MEAT SAFE, from 18s. upwards.

SULPHUR BLOWER, to destroy mildew on vines, flowers, 2s.

A SWING WASHING MACHINE, with which two boys can with ease wash any amount of dirty clothes clean.

An improved TRAP FOR CATCHING RATS, 5s.

Visitors to Selsey are respectfully invited to inspect the Factory, where all the Inventions will be cheerfully shown and explained.

Illustrated Catalogues forwarded, post free, on application.

Fig. 4 1882 Advertisement in the Sussex Advertiser "Quaint Industries and Interesting Place in Sussex".

by his trade card (Fig. 3). But it is his inventive activities (Fig. 4) that seem to have interested Colin most and led to him naming his workshop as "Colin Pullinger's Inventive Factory" (Fig. 5) And of his inventions, it his mouse traps that could catch many mice at a time that led to his fame and fortune. Both his mouse traps, the *Automaton* and the *Perpetual*, that he advertised and sold were registered with the Designs Office in 1859 (No 4158) and 1861 (No 4373) respectively[7].

Pullinger's Registered *Automaton* Mouse Trap (Fig. 6) was an ingenious but quite complex construction that was first advertised by his wholesaler (S.&E.Ransome & Co., 31 Essex Street, Strand, London) in The Ironmonger of October 31, 1860. However already by November 30, 1861, this advertisement had been replaced by one for Pullinger's Registered **Perpetual** Mouse Trap and it is this much simpler and elegant design (Fig. 7a) that became a commercial success and to which Colin subsequently made a number of minor improvements (Fig. 7b).

In the 1860s all Colin's traps had to be transported by wagon for the nine miles to the nearest railway station at Chichester for further distribution, a problem not to be overcome until the inauguration of the Selsey to Chichester Tramway in 1897. During its most productive period in the 1880s Colin Pullinger's staff of about 40 men and boys was able to turn out 960 traps a week, but by 1920 production had virtually ceased and was confined to Colin's son Charles.

Fig. 5 Colin Pullinger and his Inventive Factory

15

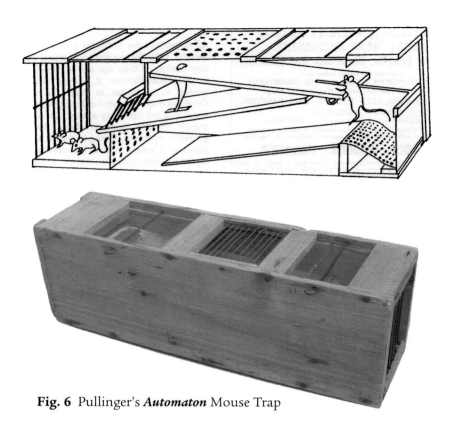

Fig. 6 Pullinger's *Automaton* Mouse Trap

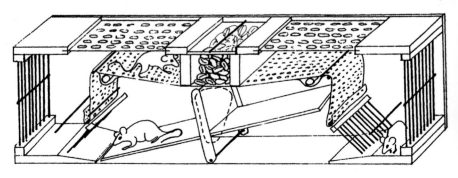

Fig. 7a Pullinger's *Perpetual* Mouse Trap – first design

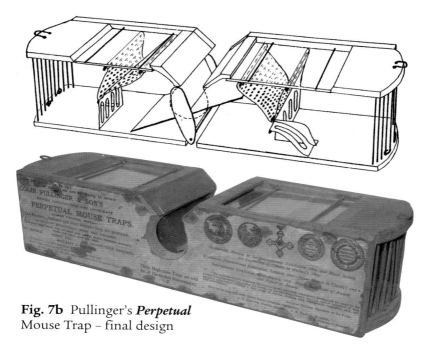

Fig. 7b Pullinger's *Perpetual*
Mouse Trap – final design

No doubt the demise of the Pullinger *Perpetual* can be blamed on the rise of effective competitors as well as the fact that Charles lacked the innovative spark of his father. Today the only evidence that remains of a Pullinger presence in Selsey is the Heritage Trail blue plaque (Fig. 8) on the Town Hall that proclaims that it stands on the site of Colin Pullinger's Inventive Factory.

Fig. 8
Pullinger's
blue plaque
at Selsey
Town Hall

Leggett & Company 1880s – 1914

Orlando Leggett, son of a blacksmith, was born in Gislingham, Suffolk in 1858. The National Census of 1881 reveals that by then he was working as a carpenter in Barking, Suffolk. By 1890 he had moved into Ipswich, where he established a business at 42 Brooks Hall Road, describing himself as a General Wood Turner, Mousetrap and Couch Manufacturer[8]. The following year saw his business specialise more and he became a Wire Worker and Mouse and Rat Trap Manufacturer[9]. His Company remained at the same Ipswich address until 1914, when it seems to have come to an end since in 1915 the address was occupied by W.J.Staines, Domestic Woodware Manufacturer[10].

The only information on what mouse traps Leggett's Company made comes from just a single surviving example of one of his catalogues[11]. This catalogue illustrates seventeen different named mouse traps that include single-catch live traps (Fig. 9), multi-catch live traps (Fig. 10) and snap and choker killing traps (Fig. 11). This variety of traps reveals that, unlike Colin Pullinger, Orlando Leggett was not an inventor, but a maker of simple traditional mouse traps, as well as a copier of more complex recent multi-catch designs, including Pullinger's **Perpetual**. The origin of the other multi-catch traps (**Acme, Premier** and **Excelsior**), involving a see-saw leading through a one-way door to a holding chamber, is unknown, but they were probably further developments of the simpler see-saw trap already illustrated (Figs 2i and j).

It seems very unlikely that Leggett and Company was the only firm in the whole of Britain specialising in the making of recently designed multi-catch and the more traditional mouse traps during this time, especially as a number of wholesale and retail hardware companies[12] advertised in their catalogues a similar array of traps, some of which were given different names. But evidence of other manufacturers is hard to find. John Turner of Sheffield Wire Works advertised a **Perfection** Mouse Trap in 1877 that was identical to Leggett's **Cossack** and George Abbey in his 1909 book "The Balance

Ordinary One Fall

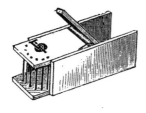

Single Hardwood Box

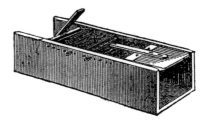

Double Hardwood Box

Free Kirk

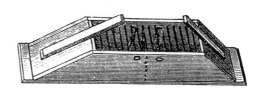

Free Kirk Double

H.G. Extra Strong

H.G. Extra Strong Double

Fig. 9 Leggett's Single-catch Live Mouse Traps –
using the names and illustrations from his catalogue

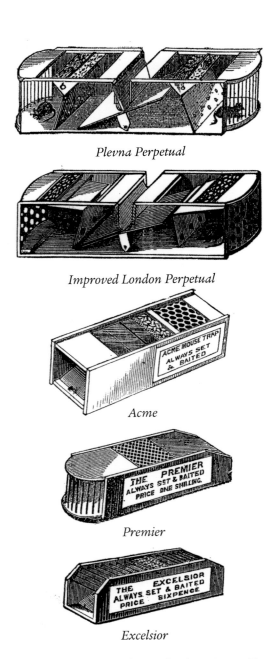

Plevna Perpetual

Improved London Perpetual

Acme

Premier

Excelsior

Fig. 10 Leggett's Single-catch Live Mouse Traps – using the names and illustrations from his catalogue

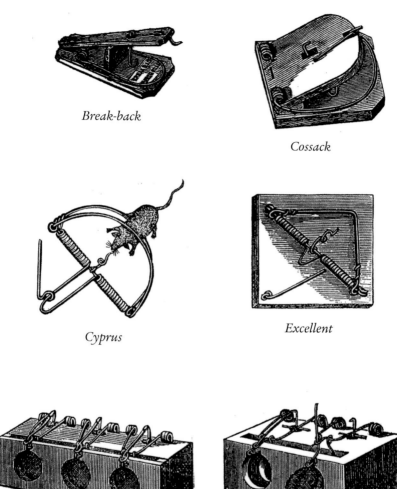

Break-back

Cossack

Cyprus

Excellent

Improved Irish
made with 1 2 3 4 5 6 holes

Improved Irish
with one mouse caught

Fig. 11 Leggett's Snap and Choker Mouse Traps –
using the names and illustrations from his catalogue

of Nature" mentions that J.J.Thomas of Edgeware Road, London, made **Acme, Premier, Excelsior** and **Perpetual** Mouse Traps.

There are very few examples of the types of traps that Leggett & Co. made that have survived to the present day (Fig. 12) and since none of them bear any identifying mark we cannot be sure who made them. Except, that is, for a few hundred small wooden single-catch live traps made recently in the 1990s by Fred Armstrong of Low Bentham, Cumbria and retailed in nearby Kirkby Lonsdale. His work is recognisable from the fact that the door and its lever was made from a single piece of wood and the bait hook integral with the door lever hook was fashioned from a strip of sheet metal rather than from wire (Fig. 12b). We will see in the next section that the same type of trap was also made by the National Patent Company at least until 1941. Both this last Company and Leggett seem to have been concerned with making improvements to **Irish** Mouse Traps, but not making the original version themselves. But there must have been contemporary mouse trap makers making unimproved **Irish** Mouse Traps. Traps designated **Irish** at this time were choker traps of the type already illustrated (Fig. 2e). Setting an **Irish** Mouse Trap was a very fiddly business because at each hole a thread had to be inserted through two small holes to tie down the overhead spring. Since there is no evidence that these mouse traps were ever made in Ireland, the origin of the name remains obscure[13]. Leggett's **Improved Irish** (Fig. 12g) replaced the thread setting/release mechanism with a wire one powered at each mouse hole by a pair of small helical springs.

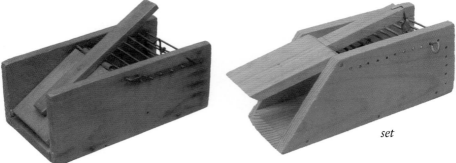

set

Fig. 12a *Ordinary One Fall*   **Fig. 12b *Free Kirk*** – recent

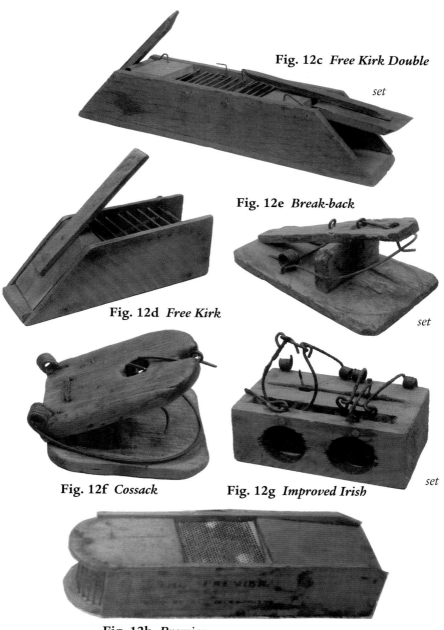

Fig. 12c *Free Kirk Double*

set

Fig. 12e *Break-back*

Fig. 12d *Free Kirk*

set

Fig. 12f *Cossack*

Fig. 12g *Improved Irish*

set

Fig. 12h *Premier*

Fig. 12 Some surviving examples of Leggett's types of traps – using the names he used in his catalogue

National Patent Company[14] 1890s – 1950s

James Hunter, the founder of the company, was born in Barrhead, Renfrew in 1845. By 1868 he had married and settled in nearby Johnstone, where he and his wife, over the next twenty years or so, raised a family and ran a prosperous drapery, millinery and dress-making business. Then, seemingly quite suddenly and apparently without any previous woodworking experience, he started to design, patent and make wooden mouse traps. By 1894 he had sold his old business in Houston Square and moved to new premises in George Street, where his business prospered so well that by 1905 he was able to build his own specially designed building for making traps. It came to be known locally as The Mouse Trap Factory.

By the end of 1900 James Hunter had designed and made for sale five differently named choker mouse traps. The hardwood **Detective** (Fig. 13a) was made with two slits instead of holes to help set the gnaw-thread release mechanism and the **Never Fail** was a softwood version of the same trap. The **New Never Fail** (Fig. 13b) replaced the two slits with a single slit ending in a large hole. Both these novel methods for setting choker traps were embodied in Hunter's patent (GB7214) of May 1894. In his two later chokers, **Snap Shot** (Fig. 13c) and **New Snap Shot** (Fig. 13d), push-wire replaced gnaw-thread release mechanisms. Curiously, none of Hunter's choker traps had its name printed on it and any surviving examples can only be iden-tified by reference to his advertisements in *The Ironmonger*.

James next turned his attention to snap traps, no doubt having become aware that the new flat snap, designed and patented (US528671) by William Hooker of Abingdon, Illinois in 1894 and named the **Out O'Sight**, was a potential threat to his business. By 1899 he was making a rather similar trap with a somewhat similar name, the **Unseen** (Fig. 14a). There then followed a whole series of flat snap traps, the **Hero**, **Veto**, **Dart**, **Million**, **Allwire**, **Nap**, **Ace**, **Baitlock**, **Betta** and **Cheapa** (Figs 14b-l), most of which only differed from one another in the nature of their bait hooks. In 1912 the bait hook for one of these, the *Veto*, was registered as a Design (No.610,372) and the name of the

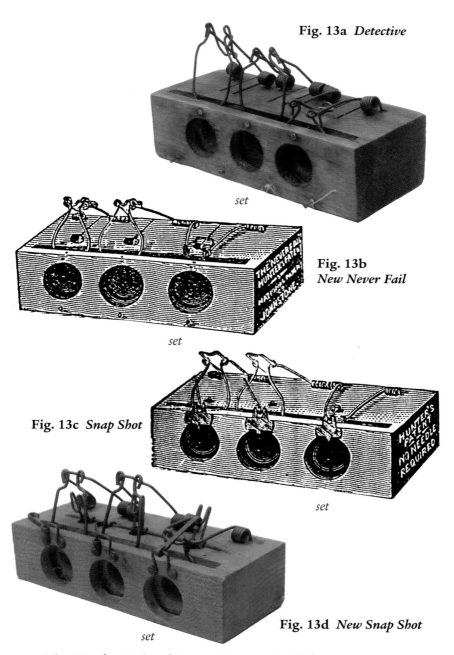

Fig. 13a *Detective*

set

Fig. 13b
New Never Fail

set

Fig. 13c *Snap Shot*

set

Fig. 13d *New Snap Shot*

set

Fig. 13 The National Patent Company's Choker Mouse Traps

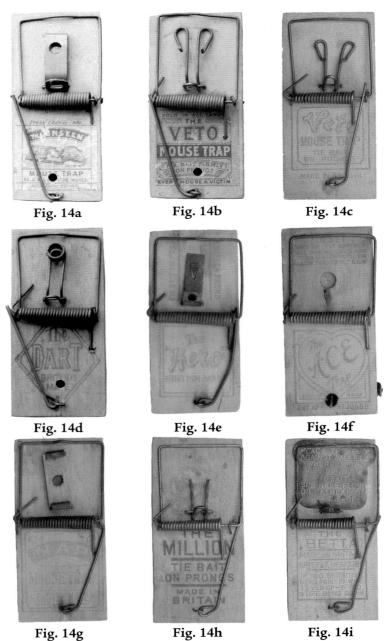

Fig. 14a　　　　　Fig. 14b　　　　　Fig. 14c

Fig. 14d　　　　　Fig. 14e　　　　　Fig. 14f

Fig. 14g　　　　　Fig. 14h　　　　　Fig. 14i

Fig. 14 Mouse Snap Traps made by the National Patent Company

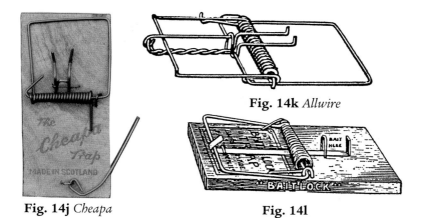

Fig. 14k *Allwire*

Fig. 14j *Cheapa*

Fig. 14l

trap registered as a Trade Mark (No.347,026). A further three of the traps were patented. The **Hero**, for which the whole base of the trap acted as a treadle, was patented by James Hunter in1899 (GB15106). After the death of the founder in 1924, the National Patent Company continued to be a family run concern, and in 1932 his son, James Barr Hunter, patented the somewhat similar but simpler mechanism used in the Ace (GB383501). Finally in 1943, Alexander Leask, Works Manager, patented the expanded metal treadle used in the **Betta** (GB566423 and 570386). One or two of the earliest snap traps were provided with paper labels (Figs 14a and b), but thereafter all had their names printed directly onto their wooden bases.

In addition to the series of snap traps mentioned above, the Company made at least three snap traps for other companies with the same treadle design as the **Million**. One was for Woolworth printed with the letter "W" within a lozenge shaped frame (Fig 15a), another for an Australian firm inscribed "Specially made in Britain for Mitchell's the Brush People" (Fig. 15b) and another presumably for Procter Bros with the word **Sentry** within a circle (Fig. 15c). That all these traps were made by the National Patent Company is revealed by its unique method of using a large staple inserted beneath the trap (Fig. 15d) to hold the spring securely in place. Also added here is a specially printed version of the **Betta** made for sale

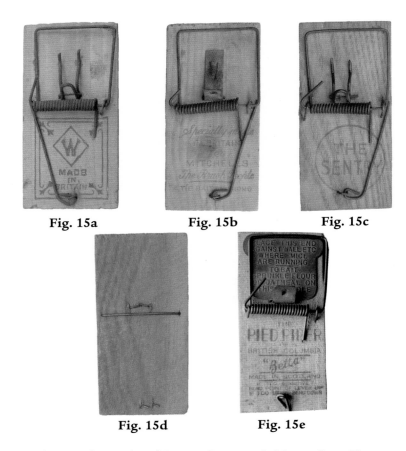

Fig. 15a Fig. 15b Fig. 15c

Fig. 15d Fig. 15e

Fig. 15 The National Patent Company's Mouse Snap Traps
made for other companies

in British Columbia and named the ***Pied Piper*** (Fig. 15e). As well as
its specially designed snap and choker traps, the factory also made
two traditional designs of small wooden single-catch live traps that
it named ***Captors*** (Fig. 16).

On Friday, 16 March 1951, the Johnstone Mouse Trap Factory
suffered a severe fire, a catastrophe from which the company never
recovered, and it was officially wound up in August 1960. The two
story building was eventually in 1984 converted into fourteen apart-
ments and so it remains to this day.

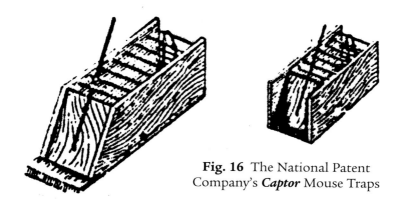

Fig. 16 The National Patent Company's *Captor* Mouse Traps

Procter Bros 1890s – Present

The firm of Procter Brothers (Wireworks) Ltd was established in Leeds in 1740, but it was not until the late 1890s that it became involved with the promotion and sale of the products of local inventor and mouse trap maker James Henry Atkinson. James was an ironmonger of 196 Hunslet Road, Leeds, who already had patented a window blind pulley (1886) and a candlestick holder (1897) when he applied for a patent for a mouse trap in December 1898. The patent (GB27488) was accepted on 4 March, 1899 and was in January of the same year already being advertised and sold by Procter Bros as the *Little Nipper*[15]. Because of the need to cut the treadle from the base of the trap, the base itself is about twice as thick as that of most other mouse snap traps.

Like Hunter's *Unseen*, Atkinson's *Little Nipper* was a modification of Hooker's flat snap trap, the *Out O'Sight*, but instead of relying on a mouse being attracted to a bait, it was designed with a treadle cut out of the whole width of the base and hinged to it, so that the trap would be readily sprung simply by the mouse running over the treadle. Nevertheless the treadle initially was provided with a hole in which to place bait (Fig. 17a). Shortly afterwards the hole was replaced by a short wire bait spike. This neat innovative design with only minor modifications to the wiring of the treadle to the base (Figs 17b-d) is still in production by Procter Brothers today. The printing

29

on the trap has also undergone little change except when included with a special promotion of "Protector Products" with the head of Oliver Cromwell (Fig. 17e) or specially made to be sold by other companies (Figs 17f and g), one of which was named *Ikat-chem* (Fig. 17h).

It appears that from 1900 James Atkinson was working for Procter Bros, since from that year all Atkinson's traps were advertised as being made by this company. In 1918, when James retired, the company acquired his premises, then at 18 Great Wilson Street, his remaining stock of traps and all his trap-making machinery, and continued to make Atkinson's series of traps. As well as the *Little Nipper* such traps included two others, the *Alert* and the *Sentry*, both of which relied on bait hooks rather than treadles to release the striking frame and catch the mice.

Atkinson applied for a patent in June 1899 for the *Alert* and it was accepted in April 1900 (GB13277), presumably for its new bait hook design (Figs 18a and 19a). No examples of this design seem to have survived, but judging by advertisements it continued to be made at least until 1922. However by 1933 the *Alert* had been given a new bait hook (Figs 18b and 19c) that seemed to be the same as Atkinson's Registered Design (No.832376) of 1914 (Fig. 19b), except that the small bait box surrounding the bait hook had been dispensed with. In 1938 the trap was fitted with a safety catch that was only released when the trap was placed on the floor and in this form was named the *Safety Alert* (Figs 18c and d). The safety device was designed and patented in 1939 (GB498490) by Alan Miller of Walsall. Thereafter the manufacture of both the *Alert* and the *Safety Alert* seems to have been discontinued.

Atkinson did not patent his *Sentry* mouse trap (Figs 20a-e) but he did register the two bait hook/treadle designs that he used in its construction. The first made of wood and wire (Figs 20a and 19d) he registered in 1904 (No. 442863). The second made from a single length of wire (Figs 20b and 19e) he registered in 1907 (No. 510977). Subsequently (c.1926) the *Sentry* bait hook was changed to a simpler wire hook with two prongs (Figs 20c and d and 19f) and much later (c.1992) the two prongs were formed from sheet metal (Figs 20e and 19g).

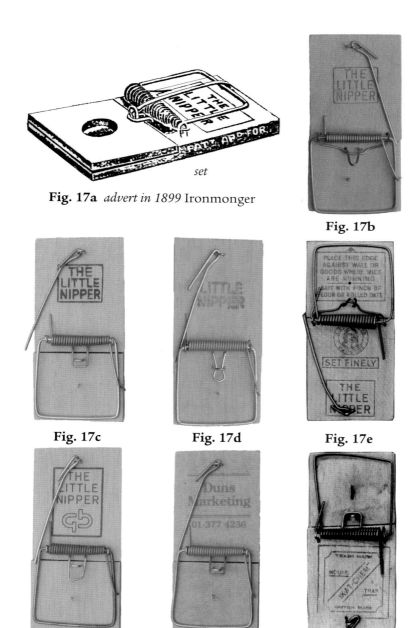

Fig. 17a *advert in 1899* Ironmonger

set

Fig. 17b

Fig. 17c

Fig. 17d

Fig. 17e

Fig. 17f

Fig. 17g

Fig. 17h

Fig. 17 Procter Brothers' **Little Nipper** and related mouse traps

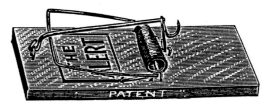

Fig. 18a

Fig. 18b

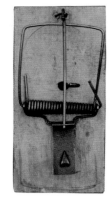

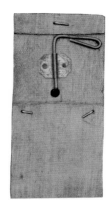

Fig. 18 Procter
Brothers' *Alert*
and *Safety Alert*

Fig. 18c   **Fig. 18d**

Sentry-design traps made for other companies include those made for Lincoln Bros of London[16] named *Victory* (Figs 20f and g), those made for Rentokil named *Rentokil* (Fig. 20h) and a one-off with a thick base printed "*Glenfiddich Haggis* Trap Mk. 111" (Figs 20i and j), no doubt for a special Scotch Whisky celebration at Hogmanay. Manufacture of the *Sentry* was discontinued in 2007.

Another wooden mouse trap made by Procter Bros, the *Felix* (Fig. 21a), was a trap that could be set by simply pressing down the striking frame into a notch. It was designed by Hubert Haywood of Matlock and patented (GB762248) by him in 1956. It was advertised in *Benn's Encyclopedia* from 1956-1963. Another Procter-made mouse trap was the *Nippit* (Fig. 21b) with an aluminium base, manufactured from 1936 to 1954.

Following a move from Leeds to a factory in Cardiff Docks (1938) and another to Caerphilly (!946), Procter Brothers finally in

1970 moved their trap-making operations to Bedwas, Gwent, where today the only traps they manufacture are Atkinson's wooden **Little Nipper** and the plastic single-catch live **Trip-Trap**. The original manufacturer in the 1980s of the **Trip-Trap** was North West Plastics Ltd of Manchester, who were taken over by Stewart Plastics who later in 1990 passed on the production and marketing of the trap to Procter Bros. Its inventor, Maurice Juggins, was born in 1934 in Bromsgrove, Worcestershire. He worked as a Chartered Engineer, first in the aircraft industry and later in his own design business, eventually becoming Director of Studies of Postgraduate Industrial Design at Birmingham Polytechnic. During his professional career he invented and patented a number of improved designs for a number of useful domestic products. It was therefore not surprising

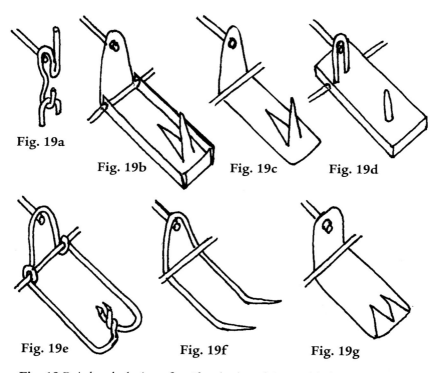

Fig. 19a

Fig. 19b

Fig. 19c

Fig. 19d

Fig. 19e

Fig. 19f

Fig. 19g

Fig. 19 Bait hook designs for *Alert* (a-c) and *Sentry* (d-g) mouse traps

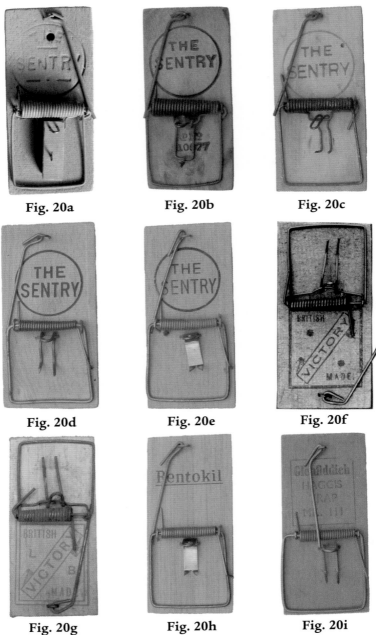

Fig. 20a

Fig. 20b

Fig. 20c

Fig. 20d

Fig. 20e

Fig. 20f

Fig. 20g

Fig. 20h

Fig. 20i

Fig. 20 Procter Brothers' *Sentry* and related mouse traps

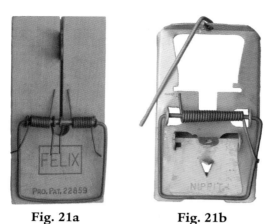

Fig. 21a   **Fig. 21b**

Fig. 21 Procter Brothers' *Felix* and *Nippit* mouse traps

that, when faced with having to help his neighbour by rescuing a mouse caught by one leg in a snap trap, that his thoughts turned to inventing a humane mouse trap, especially as at the time such a trap was no longer readily available in Britain for use by householders.

Maurice's first design was a simple plastic box trap with a push-up door, for which he applied for a patent in 1979, the patent being granted in 1982 (GB 2017477). However its success was not to his satisfaction and his next design incorporated an internal swing-down door that closed fast only after a mouse had passed it and released it by stepping on a treadle. This design was covered by two patents published in 1984 (GB 2017477 and GB 2095087) and included a separate removable container at the end of the trap that was either small in size (Fig. 22a) for the capture of house mice or much larger (Figs 22b and c) to contain nest material when the trap was being used for outdoor studies of field mice and voles. Later on in 1996 to make the traps even more humane Maurice Juggins introduced three ventilation holes (Fig. 22d) situated on each side of the trap in a place where the trapped mice would be unable to use them to gnaw their way out (GB 2292063).

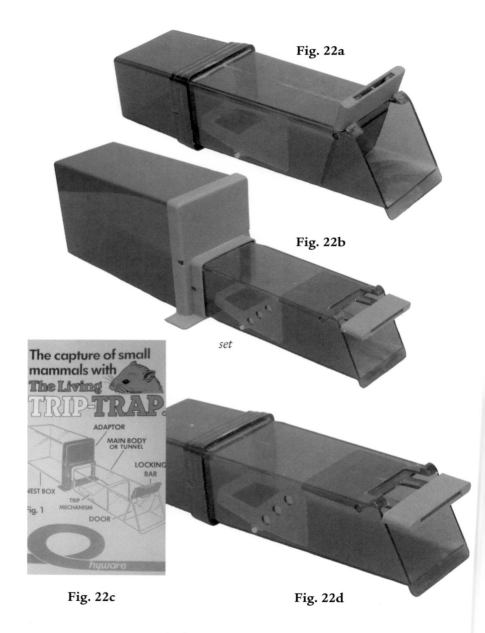

Fig. 22a

Fig. 22b

set

The capture of small
mammals with
The Living
TRIP-TRAP.

ADAPTOR

MAIN BODY
OR TUNNEL

LOCKING
BAR

NEST BOX

Fig. 1

TRIP
MECHANISM

DOOR

hyware

Fig. 22c

Fig. 22d

Fig. 22 *Trip-Trap* mouse trap

36

Fig. 23 Procter Brothers' Pest-Stop *Baitless* mouse trap

Procter Brothers also market another British designed mouse trap the Pest-Stop *Baitless* (Fig. 22). This trap is a black plastic tunnel with a treadle and striking frame contained within it and an external setting lever that also helpfully indicates when a set trap has caught a mouse. Apart from not requiring to be baited, a further unusual feature is that the spring and part of its release mechanism is housed in a sealed compartment along side the tunnel so that it cannot be disturbed by a mouse before entering the trap. It was designed by Simon Levesley of Leezli Product Design, Fradley, Staffordshire, and is manufactured in China.

All the other mouse traps not mentioned above that are currently marketed by Procter Bros under the Trade Mark "Pest-Stop" are designed and made overseas and are dealt with briefly later.

Fig. 24a

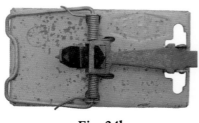

Fig. 24b

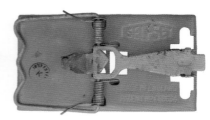

Fig. 24c

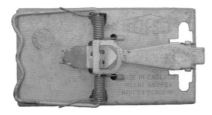

Fig. 24d

Fig. 24e

Fig. 24f

Fig. 24g

Fig. 24 *Selfset* mouse traps

Selfset Ltd 1950s – Present

Selfset Limited of Falcon Works, 39 Hanworth Road, Sunbury-on-Thames, Middlesex, was a company set up in the 1950s specially to manufacture and sell an all-metal snap trap to the design of Richard Henry Evans of Surbiton, Surrey. At the time Richard Evans, employed by Babcock and Wilcox, was already a designer of high quality precision-engineered products.

In the late 1940s Richard Evans, unable to quell an infestation of mice in his garage at his home in Surbiton using the then available snap traps, observed that his mice tended to push at the bait on the hook rather than pull on it[17] He therefore decided to design a trap with this aspect of mouse behaviour in mind. He applied for a patent in March, 1949 and the complete specification was published in March 1952 (GB668634).

The first *Selfsets* to be made had a metal base painted green as had some later ones with some minor design changes (Figs 24b and c). Thereafter they were all made of galvanised metal and a few other design changes occurred (Figs 24d-g), for some of which the company were granted a further patent in 1966 (GB1034696). The design of the box (Fig. 24a) in which individual traps were sold has remained unchanged.

The Company, naming Richard Evans as the inventor, also patented in 1965 (GB 1000538) a quite different all-metal mouse trap that had the whole base acting as a treadle. This trap was named the *Trapsit* (Figs 25a and b) and was made and sold by the Company until Rentokil arranged to retail the entire production, when, at any rate on the packaging, the trap was renamed the *Rentokil* mouse trap and the package design changed from time to time (Figs 25c-e). Its production was discontinued in the1990s.

Fig. 25a

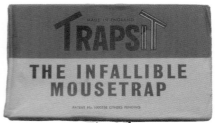

Fig. 25b

Fig. 25c

Fig. 25d

Fig. 25e

Fig. 25 *Trapsit* mouse traps

Other Manufacturers

Apart from the five major successful mouse trap makers already described, only two of whom are still in business, there were quite a few others who seem to have been somewhat less commercially successful, at any rate in making mouse traps. These will now be dealt with in what is believed to be more or less the correct chronological order and it will soon become apparent that the mouse trap production of most of the earliest ones can only be deduced from the advertisements that were placed in trade journals.

G.H.Ellis

Ellis's **Self-Acting** mouse trap was reviewed in *The Ironmonger* of April 30, 1861 (Fig. 26). It was subsequently advertised by G.H.Ellis of Malton, Yorkshire, in the same journal in the same year in the following months of May, June, October and December, but not thereafter. In his advertisements Ellis describes himself as inventor, patentee and manufacturer, but I have been unable to discover any patent registered under his name.

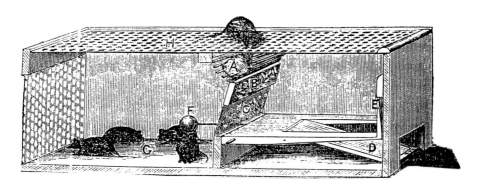

Fig. 26 Ellis's **Self-Acting** mouse trap

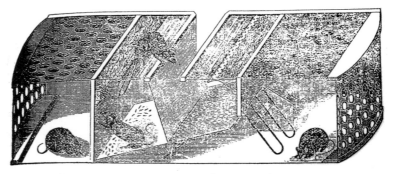

Fig. 27 Bennetts's *Improved Perpetual* mouse trap

Bennett & Co.

Bennett & Co. of Cannon Street, London advertised its *Improved Perpetual* mouse trap in *The Ironmonger* of May 31, 1867 (Fig. 27). This early modification of Pullinger's *Perpetual* is only known from this single advertisement. The main improvement was to narrow the internal one-way door so that a single mouse entering the holding chamber would not allow already trapped mice to escape. Interestingly Pullinger later incorporated this improvement into his own trap design.

Fig. 28 Colbran & Pollard's *Self-Acting Perpetual* mouse trap

Colbran & Pollard

John Colbran and William Pollard, both of 5 Holloway, Middlesex applied for a patent for their improved trap in March 1870 and it was approved in September of the same year (GB853). They named their trap as the new *Self-acting Perpetual* and advertised it (Fig. 28) in *The Ironmonger* for the four months of August September, October and November in 1871. The trap is only known from these advertisements.

Joseph Wilcox

Joseph Wilcox of Newtown Wire Works, Birmingham, describes himself as General Wire Weaver, Drawer and Manufacturer of numerous wire goods including rat and mouse traps. His only known mouse trap is figured in the Martineau & Smith's Hardware Trade Journal of February 28, 1880. Here it is described as a ***Patent Gauze*** mouse trap (Fig. 29) and can be seen to be a metal three-in-a-row version of a traditional wooden box trap.

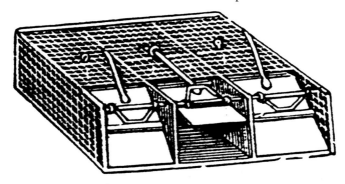

Fig. 29 Joseph Wilcock's ***Patent Gauze*** mouse trap

Cheap Wood Company

The ***Iron*** Bird or Mouse trap (Fig. 30a) made by the Cheap Wood Company is only known from an advertisement in the 1902 catalogue of Harding & Sons of London. It is figured with a number of other traps under the wording "Having purchased the whole of the remaining stock of these Patent Traps from the Receiver of the Cheap Wood Company we offer as under to clear". I have been unable to find any patent for the trap.

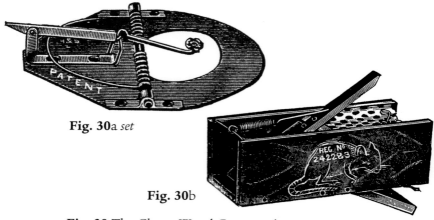

Fig. 30a *set*

Fig. 30b

Fig. 30 The Cheap Wood Company's mouse traps

The Cheap Wood Company presumably also made the trap advertised as the **Cheap Wood** mouse trap (Fig. 30b) in the 1902 Catalogue of Johnson, Clapham and Morris, Manufacturers, Merchants and Hardware Factors of Manchester. This trap, only known from this advertisement, was patented in July 1896 (application in November, 1895) (GB21396) by Richard Whitaker a Hardware Merchant of Manchester. The main difference between Whitaker's trap and those small wooden box traps of the type being made by Leggett was that the bait hook was not removable and the bait was placed on the hook through a hinged section in the trap floor. Whitaker registered this design (Des242283) as well as patenting it.

Fig. 31 *Terror* mouse trap

John Williams & Son

Joseph Williams Senior and Junior traded under the name of John Williams & Son, a well established steel trap making firm of

Wednesfield, Staffordshire[18]. They made an all-steel mouse trap named the **Terror** (Fig. 31) with a hole beneath the treadle, allowing it to be pushed up from below. A patent for the trap design was applied for by the makers in June 1905 and accepted in March 1906 (GB11476).

Rotary Trap Company

The **Rotary** automatic mouse exterminator (Fig. 32) is known only from advertisements placed by its maker, the Rotary Trap Company of Walsall, Staffordshire, in *The Ironmonger* (October 27, 1906 and March 30, 1907). An earlier advertisement (*The Ironmonger* of March 31, 1906) named the trap as the **Perpetual** and its maker as the Perpetual Trap Company. Its designer, George Lavender of Aldridge, Staffordshire, applied for a patent in November, 1905 and it was granted in March, 1906 (GB 23651). The patent reveals that the internal mechanism of the trap consisted of four revolving platforms. A mouse entering the trap and attempting to take the bait would release a catch that would tip the mouse into a water container below and the next platform would take the place of the first and be ready for the next mouse.

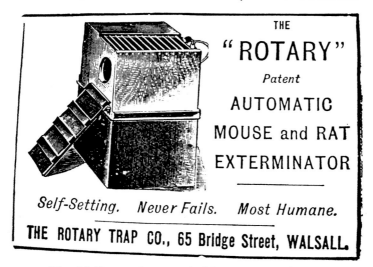

THE "ROTARY" Patent AUTOMATIC MOUSE and RAT EXTERMINATOR

Self-Setting. Never Fails. Most Humane.

THE ROTARY TRAP CO., 65 Bridge Street, WALSALL.

Fig. 32 *Rotary* Automatic Mouse Exterminator

Fig. 33 Simpson Tank mouse trap

Simpson & Sons

The **Simpson Tank** mouse trap (Fig. 33) is known only from a single advertisement placed by its maker, Simpson & Sons of Otley, Yorkshire, in *The Ironmonger* of March 1, 1913. Francis Simpson, Ironmonger of Horsforth, Yorkshire, applied for a patent for his trap design in April, 1911 and it was accepted in November of the same year (GB21596).

W.T.French & Son

W.T. French & Son of the Mysto Works, Birmingham, advertised their **Mysto** automatic mouse trap in *Benn's Encyclopedia* of 1917 (Fig. 34). It is only known from this one advertisement, but it looks to have been a very good copy of Carl Bender's German-made **Capito**[19].

Owen Wilks

Owen Wilks, brickmaker of Galley Hill Brickyard, Banbury, Oxfordshire, made a very unusual mouse trap made of baked brick clay that he named the **Tip-Top** (Fig. 35). A mouse taking the bait released a spherical ball of clay that would drop down and crush the mouse.

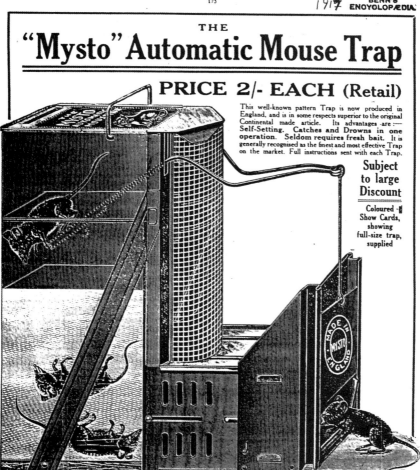

THE
"Mysto" Automatic Mouse Trap

PRICE 2/- EACH (Retail)

This well-known pattern Trap is now produced in England, and is in some respects superior to the original Continental made article. Its advantages are :— Self-Setting. Catches and Drowns in one operation. Seldom requires fresh bait. It is generally recognised as the finest and most effective Trap on the market. Full instructions sent with each Trap.

Subject
to large
Discount

Coloured
Show Cards,
showing
full-size trap,
supplied

W. T. FRENCH & SON

HORTICULTURAL AND SURGICAL BRASSFOUNDERS AND SPRAYER SPECIALISTS, TIN AND COPPERSMITHS,

HEAD OFFICE AND WORKS: TIN AND COPPERSMITH WORKS:
ST. MARY STREET.   JOHNSTONE STREET and
                            "MYSTO" WORKS, BROWNING STREET.

LADYWOOD, BIRMINGHAM.

Telephone—384 Edgbaston, B'ham.   Telegrams—"Syringes," B'ham.

Fig. 34 The *Mysto* Automatic mouse trap

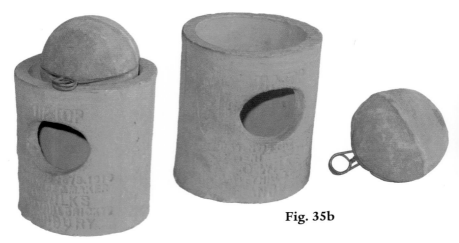

Fig. 35b

Fig. 35a *set*   **Fig. 35** The *Tip-Top* mouse trap

Owen Wilks applied for a patent for his trap design in December 1919 and it was accepted in June 1920 (GB144575). He inscribed the trap with his name and address, the name of the trap and its patent number. Quite unusually for a British trap maker, he also a little later took out a French patent (FR529119) that was approved in November 1921.

B. Winstone & Sons Ltd

B. Winstone & Sons of Shoe Lane, London was evidently one of several manufacturers of glue to trap rats and mice in the 1920s[20]. Its product named *Ratsticker* was sold in tins (Fig. 36) printed with directions for use. The tin should first be placed in boiling water and when the glue is warm it should be poured onto the centre of a thick piece of cardboard

Fig. 36 *Ratsticker* mouse glue

15 inches square. Once the glue has spread over the board a piece of cheese or other bait should be placed in its centre and the board positioned near rat or mouse holes and runs.

Mark Patent Company

In August 1920, William Mark, a builder of Great Corby near Carlisle, and Frederic Parker, an ironmonger of Carlisle, Cumberland, applied for a patent for their newly designed all-metal mouse trap that they named *Ezi-set* (Fig. 37). The patent (GB171493) was accepted in November 1921. The name of the maker of the trap, the Mark Patent Company, presumably established by William Mark, is only deduced from the fact that this English Company was granted a French patent (FR539289) for the same trap design in 1922.

The trap was advertised in the 1929 catalogue of H. Thompson of Norwich and in the catalogues of the Army & Navy Stores Ltd,

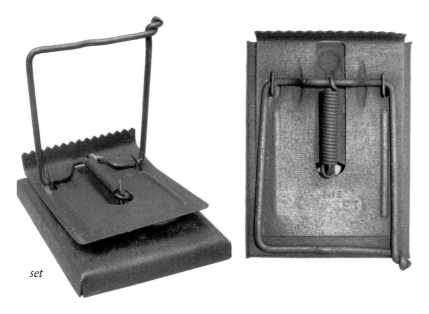

set

Fig. 37 The *Ezi-set* mouse trap

London, from 1925-1936[21]. In 1931 James Ritchie extolled its merits in a book on farm pests[22]. Ritchie thought the design superior to wooden break-back traps in its weather-proof quality, its simplicity of setting, its adjustable sensitiveness and the ease with which the trap could be taken apart and cleaned. Although he figures an *Ezi-Set* mouse trap, his remarks seemed to have been aimed rather more at the much larger *Ezi-Set* rat trap.

S. Young & Sons (Misterton) Ltd

This Misterton Company was founded by Samuel Young in 1895 and until 1992 dealt in a great variety of "Sporting Appliances and Sundries", some of which it manufactured itself[23]. The first of four mouse traps that were made was a wooden box live trap advertised as capable of catching more than "Twenty mice in one Night". When I bought one of these traps in 1991 George Young, then 85 and Samuel's sole surviving son, told me that when at the age of 13 he started working in the family firm, this was the type of trap that he had first made. In 1940 the trap was called the *Top Hole* mouse trap (Fig. 38a), but by 1972 the trap had been slightly redesigned and renamed the *Auto* mouse trap (Fig. 38b). The same trap with the same name and made to the same design (Fig. 38c) is now being made by John Dee Humane Traps of Woodbury Salterton, Devon. An identical trap has also been made by Fuller Engineering Limited and named the *Fuller Mouse Box*.

The other three mouse traps advertised seem to have been much less successful. The *Silent Killer* (Fig. 39a), a wire-mesh version of Carl Bender's German *Capito*[19] was advertised in a 1930s catalogue, along with a wire-mesh cage trap named the *Automatic Catch-All* (Fig. 39b), that was also advertised in 1940. No examples of either of these traps seem to have survived. Finally the *Four-in-One* (Fig. 40), designed to catch mice, cockroaches, wasps, flies, moles, slugs and woodlice, figured in Young's 1972 catalogue. The trap design was patented by Stephen Hussey of Bagborough, Somerset in 1940 (GB526444).

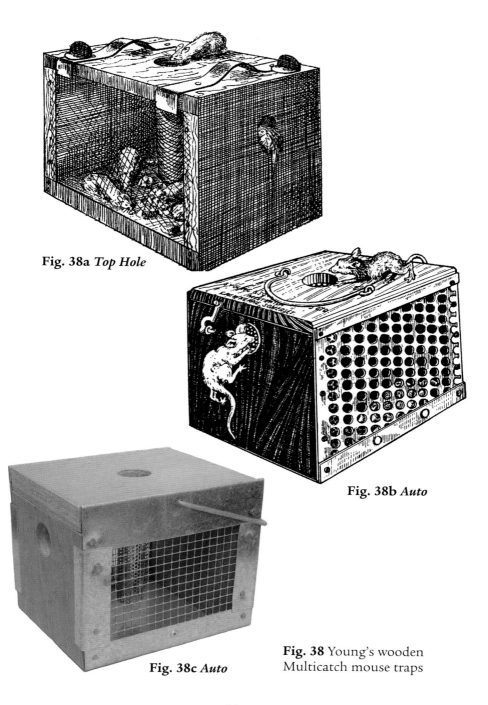

Fig. 38a *Top Hole*

Fig. 38b *Auto*

Fig. 38c *Auto*

Fig. 38 Young's wooden Multicatch mouse traps

51

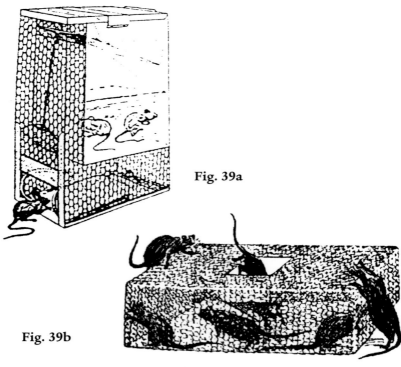

Fig. 39a

Fig. 39b

Fig. 39 Young's *Silent Killer* (a) and *Automatic Catch-All* (b)

Fig. 40 *Four-in-One*

Gripper Manufacturing Company

This Company made a variety of "Gripper" traps for various animals from 1914-1969[24]. In one of its advertisements, probably in the 1930s, it promoted the **Gripper** mouse trap in the following terms: "This is an ordinary break-back trap of wood with a bait-prong release; but it has a ring connecting the lever to the staple to allow the jaw to be slightly raised when the trap is set. It kills the poor little wretches instantly. (*Specially recommended by the R.S.P.C.A.*)". The advertisement then adds "Gripper mouse traps cannot be made at present; so in the meantime use ordinary break-back traps with a bait-prong release. Avoid using those with a platform release, as they often torture a mouse without killing it".

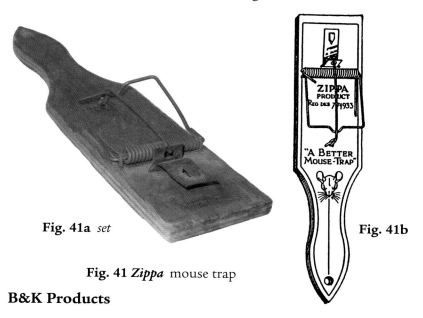

Fig. 41a *set*

Fig. 41b

Fig. 41 *Zippa* mouse trap

B&K Products

Percival Baxter, trading as B&K Products of Birmingham, registered the design of his **Zippa** mouse trap (Fig. 41a) in July 1932 (No.774933). His Company went bankrupt in 1934. The trap was advertised (Fig. 41b) in the 1935 Catalogue of Crowden & Keeves Ltd of London.

Allcock Manufacturing Company

The *Prong* mouse trap was designed by William Carpenter and James Crawford of Birkenhead, Cheshire. They applied for a patent in May 1945 and it was accepted in April 1948 (GB600323). They also registered the design with the patent office (Design No843674).The trap was made in Birkenhead by a branch of the Allcock Manufacturing Company of Ossining, New York, who also registered the Trade Mark "PRONG" in June 1946.

This green-enamelled all-metal mouse trap with its set/release mechanism mainly housed below in its hollow base appeared in two forms. In the first (Figs 42a and b), the rod beneath the trap connected to the bait treadle had a hook at the other end that emerged

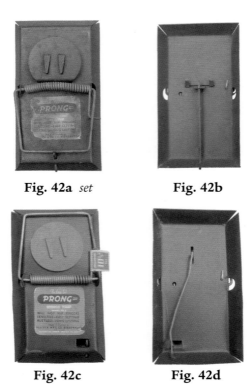

Fig. 42a *set*   **Fig. 42b**

Fig. 42c   **Fig. 42d**

Fig. 42 *Prong* mouse trap

in the centre of the end of the trap base. When set, the striking frame lodged beneath this hook (Fig. 42a). In its later form shown unset (Figs 42c and d) the bait treadle and connecting rod have been rust-proofed and the hook to engage with the striking frame now emerges in one corner of the trap base.

Fig. 43a   **Fig. 43**b *set*

Fig. 43 *Klik* mouse trap

Dandridge Product

The metal ***Klik*** mouse trap was made by Dandridge Product of Loughton, Essex. A patent was applied for in October, 1949, by the trap designer, George Dandridge of Sylvan Works, Baldwins Hill, Loughton, and it was accepted in September, 1951 (GB657259). The trap was first made in three separate colours, orange, green and blue (Fig. 43a) and was printed with its name and "PAT APP" on its base and the word "FAERY" , with some indecipherable figures above and below, on its treadle. After acceptance of the patent the base was printed with "Klik Dandridge Product, Loughton, England" and the treadle with "Brit Pat Faery 657259" (Fig. 43b). The significance of the word "Faery" remains unknown. George Dandridge was also granted a patent for the trap design in the USA in October 1953 (US 2656641), but there is no evidence that the trap was ever made or sold there.

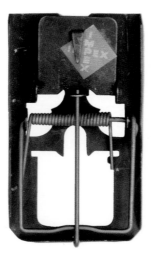

Fig. 44 *Impex* mouse trap

H. Stanley Bleyer Ltd

The *Impex* mouse trap (Fig. 44) is a standard all-metal snap trap cut from a single sheet of metal, with the treadle cut out from the base and with a finger hole beneath the treadle to help set the trap. It was made at Stanley Bleyer's Impex Works in Birmingham, the name IMPEX being registered as a Trade Mark (No 676438) in March 1950. The trap was advertised in *Benn's Encyclopedia* of 1950 and 1951.

Robert Joliffe Trust

Robert Arthur Matthews can only be described as one of the most mysterious and enigmatic of British mouse trap makers and inventors. He was born in 1908 in Bury Lancashire, where his father was an electrical engineer. In 1941 and 1942 he was living in Liverpool where he published two curious pamphlets[25] in the first of which he described himself as a Radio Engineer-Inventor and in the second as an Atomic Engineer and Inventor. By 1944 he had moved to Aston Clinton in Buckinghamshire, where, under the name of Robert A. Joliffe and describing himself as Astronomer – Scientist Writer, he wrote a third pamphlet in which he revealed his belief that the planets had influenced his life in a seven year cycle and at the time of writing in February 1944 the Planet Neptune had reached its position of Maximum Beneficial Influence[26]. It seems that it was during this particularly favourable period of his life that Robert Matthews (now Joliffe) invented his electrical mouse traps and founded the Robert Joliffe Trust to manufacture them.

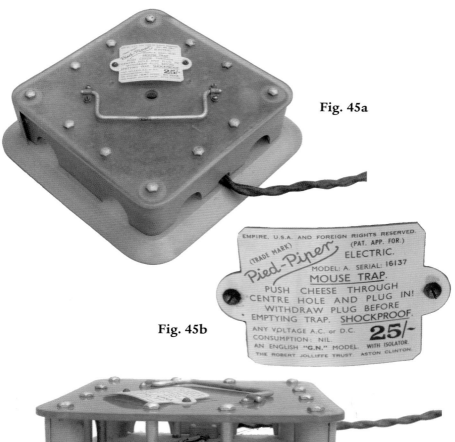

Fig. 45a

Fig. 45b

Fig. 45c

Fig. 45 *Pied Piper* electric mouse trap

57

Fig. 46 *Uranus*
electric mouse trap

Fig. 46a

Two different designs of mouse trap are known that bear the name of the Robert Joliffe Trust. The first was named the **Pied Piper** and was a large square metal box (7.5x7.5inches) with two entrance holes on each side (Fig. 45) and the second was a small tube with a single entrance at one end. The smaller one was also at first named the **Pied Piper**, but this was later changed to **Uranus** (Fig. 46), no doubt as a result of some planetary influence. The Joliffe Trust seems not to have made many traps nor to have lasted very long. Only a single large and a few small ones are known and the Buckinghamshire Public Record Office could find no evidence of the existence of the Trust in Aston Clinton. Also I have been unable to find any evidence of registration of Patents or Trade Marks. Robert Matthews died in nearby Tring, Hertfordshire, in 1987.

Fig. 46b

58

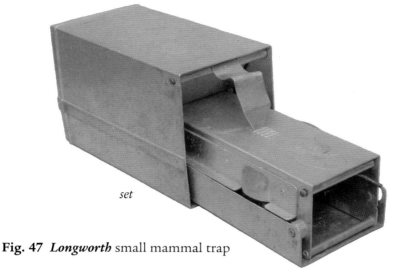

set

Fig. 47 *Longworth* small mammal trap

Longworth Scientific Instrument Company

The *Longworth* small mammal trap (Fig. 47) was made by the Longworth Scientific Instrument Company Ltd of Abingdon, Oxfordshire. The trap was made of aluminium with a swing-down door that was released when an animal trod on an internal treadle. When the door fell shut a locking bar prevented it from being reopened from the inside. Most importantly a large removable holding chamber was positioned at the end of the trap so that a trapped animal could be provided with food and nest material and kept comfortable until released. It was designed by Dennis Chitty & D.A.Kempson of the Bureau of Animal Population, Oxford University, with the specific aim of studying live animals, particularly mice and voles, in the field. They published the design of the trap and its scientific purpose and background in 1949[27] and a more practical guide to its use has been republished recently by the Mammal Society[28].

The *Longworth* trap is still being made in Abingdon, but the manufacturer is now trading under the name of Penlon Limited. In addition, the trap is also now available with a shrew-escape hole of 13mm diameter set in the nesting chamber's rear panel which is then made of chrome-plated brass to resist the gnawing of mice and voles.

set

Fig. 48 *Wellfield* small mammal trap

Wellfield

The name of the manufacturer as well as the name of the **Wellfield** small mammal trap is derived from the names of its sponsor, Ken West, its designer, Roy Ok*ell*, and the Kent village, Stalis*field*, in which they both live. The trap (Fig. 48) was made of aluminium with a stainless steel door and was designed to make it easy to manufacture and to disassemble completely for cleaning. Insertion of the rear door locked the assembly rigid and its removal made it easy to extract the trapped voles , mice and shrews.

The trap was manufactured by Wellfield from 1999 to 2003 and the possibility of further production is now in the hands of Alana Ecology of Bishop's Castle, Shropshire.

Victor Johnson

Victor Johnson of Aylsham, Norfolk, made the **Davis** small mammal trap (Fig. 49) from about 1960 until 1983 for research workers studying populations of small mammals in the field. Ron Davis of

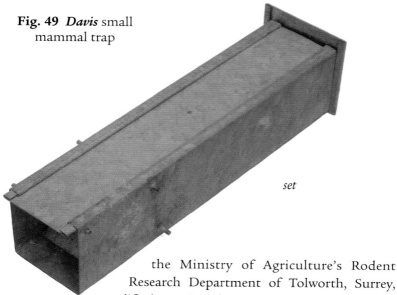

Fig. 49 *Davis* small mammal trap

set

the Ministry of Agriculture's Rodent Research Department of Tolworth, Surrey, modified an original French design and published the new design in 1961[29]. Its mechanism was similar to that of the ***Longworth***, but it had no large separate holding chamber and captive animals were released by sliding upwards the end panel of the trap. Its main advantage over the ***Longworth*** was that it was made of galvanised iron that could not be gnawed by its captives.

Philip Harris Ltd

Philip Harris of Shenstone, Staffordshire, made the ***Anderson*** small mammal trap (Fig. 50) sometime in the 1980s. It was designed by J. Anderson of the Department of Biological Sciences of Exeter University. It was made of aluminium alloy, but had no exposed metal edges for captives to gnaw upon, except for the door that was made of stainless steel. The door was hinged at the side and spring-loaded to close when activated. When closed the door revealed a hole of 14mm diameter that allowed the escape of most European species of shrew but not that of adult field mice and voles that were the target of the university's field studies.

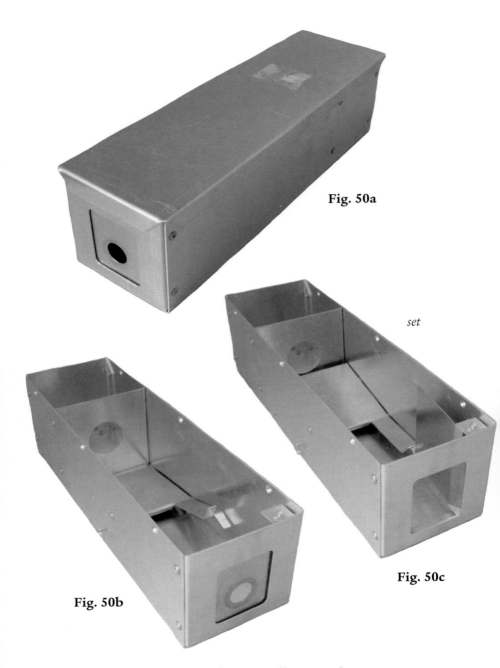

Fig. 50a

set

Fig. 50c

Fig. 50b

Fig. 50 *Anderson* small mammal traps

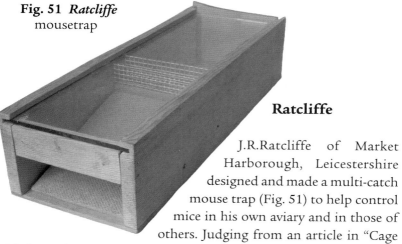

Fig. 51 *Ratcliffe*
mousetrap

Ratcliffe

J.R.Ratcliffe of Market
Harborough, Leicestershire
designed and made a multi-catch
mouse trap (Fig. 51) to help control
mice in his own aviary and in those of
others. Judging from an article in "Cage
Birds and Aviary" and correspondence in "Gamekeeper and
Countryside" he must have made quite a few over a period of some
years between 1960 and 1980[30]. His trap with its see-saw followed by
a one-way door is somewhat similar to the much earlier multi-catch
traps figured in Leggett's Catalogue. Since his trap seems not to
have been given a name, I will call it the ***Ratcliffe*** mouse trap.

Tass Products

Tass Products of Huddersfield, Yorkshire, was named from the ini-
tials of the Yorkshire farmer Thomas Albert Smith & Sons[31], who
founded the company with the specific aim of manufacturing his
mouse trap design (Fig. 52). The trap was first sold as the ***Tass***
Mousecatcher and the Trade Mark "Tass" was registered on 16 May,
1973 (No.B89767), but soon after the trap was renamed the ***Pied***
Piper and this Trade Mark was registered on November, 1973
(No.1005048). This small tubular plastic single-catch live trap had a
red ring of inwardly pointing spikes within its entrance to prevent a
trapped mouse from backing out and a removable black plastic end
in which to place bait and to allow for extracting a victim.

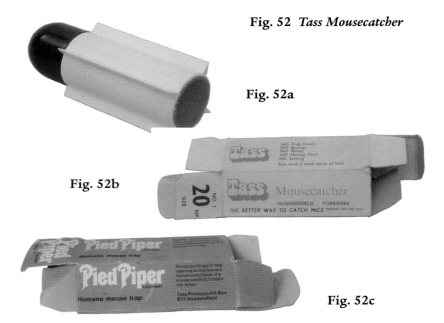

Fig. 52 *Tass Mousecatcher*

Fig. 52a

Fig. 52b

Fig. 52c

Alan Bayliss

When Alan Bayliss of Malvern, Worcestershire, was made redundant as an electrical and mechanical engineer making electronic balances, he became a bird fancier and kept birds in an aviary. His aviary became infested with mice and as a result he designed and made a multi-catch mouse trap that he named the ***Pop In*** (Fig. 53). He made and sold this trap from his house in Malvern from about 1980 until 1990 when he finally retired to the Isle of Wight.

1989 Gadgets

This manufacturer of Aberfeldy, Perthshire, made a completely transparent mouse trap (Fig. 54) that could be set to catch a single mouse alive and was then sold as ***Green Kat***. Alternatively with a slightly modified setting device it could be set to kill and was then named the ***Snap Kat***.

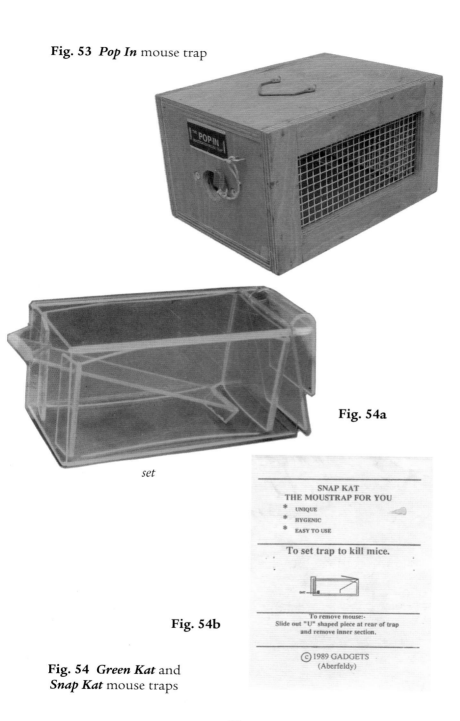

Fig. 53 *Pop In* mouse trap

Fig. 54a

set

SNAP KAT
THE MOUSTRAP FOR YOU
* UNIQUE
* HYGENIC
* EASY TO USE

To set trap to kill mice.

To remove mouse:-
Slide out "U" shaped piece at rear of trap
and remove inner section.

© 1989 GADGETS
(Aberfeldy)

Fig. 54b

Fig. 54 *Green Kat* and
Snap Kat mouse traps

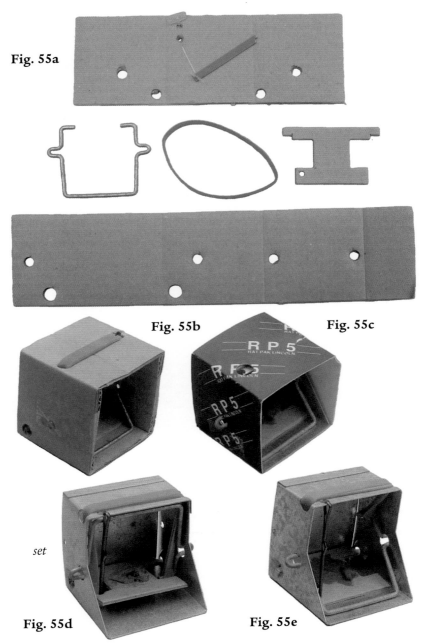

Fig. 55a

Fig. 55b   Fig. 55c

set

Fig. 55d   Fig. 55e

Fig. 55 *Rat Pak* mouse trap

Rat Pak Rodent Control Systems

The **Rat Pak** mouse trap (Fig. 55) was designed by Brian White and made in the early 1990s by his Company, Rat Pak Rodent Control Systems of Thorpe on the Hill, Lincolnshire. It was a small cardboard box snap trap powered by an elastic band and intended as a cheap throwaway product for use by the pest control industry. The first design was available as a flat pack of components (Fig.55a) for the operator to construct into a trap (Fig 55b), but later already assembled traps were available with a much stronger metal box within a cardboard cover (Fig. 55c). The same trap without the outer cover is shown set and unset (Figs 55d and e).

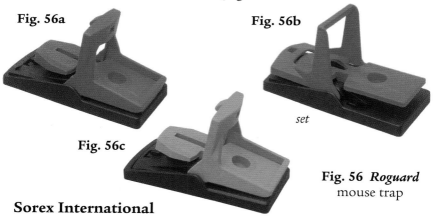

Fig. 56a

Fig. 56b

set

Fig. 56c

Fig. 56 *Roguard* mouse trap

Sorex International

Sorex International first launched their new **Roguard** mouse trap for use by the Pest Control Industry in March 2003[32]. It was designed by Network Pest Control Systems Ltd and was made in plastic with a black base and green treadle, striking and setting frames (Figs 56a and b). Another version produced for retail sale to householders had the green plastic replaced with blue (Fig. 56c). The blue version also proclaimed on its packaging that it had an alluring chocolate aroma and needed no bait. The trap was soon withdrawn and, after rectifying a small design fault, was re-launched in 2006. Production and sale of the **Roguard** mouse trap ended in 2007.

CAT Enterprises Ltd

CAT Enterprises of Wallingford, Oxfordshire, put its **Mouse-Can** trap (Fig. 57) on the market in 2005. It was designed by David Boulton of Rotherham, Yorkshire, who applied for a patent (GB 2412285A) in 2005. The design was simply a circular piece of black plastic shaped to fit on an empty food can and provided with a square push-up door ornamented with the face of a cat.

Fig. 57 *Mouse Can* mouse trap

Rentokil

Rentokil's R&D Unit has launched the Company's rodent control capability into the 21st Century by developing a mouse monitoring, trapping and killing unit named **Radar** (Fig. 58). As a mouse passes over a pressure pad in the centre of a passageway running through the trap it triggers the closure of red doors at each end of the passage and the release of carbon dioxide to quickly and humanely kill the mouse. The closure of the red doors and a red light flashing on the top of the trap reveal to the user that a mouse has been caught and that the unit needs servicing. The rodent detection apparatus in the form of a pressure pad was invented by Timothy Willets, Mark Gregory and Colin Smith and a patent (WO9818318) was granted to Rentokil in 1998. The means for releasing the carbon dioxide from an aerosol container was designed by Trevor Lawson, Andrew Brigham, Michael Best and Martin Robert-Jones and patented by Rentokil in 2004 (GB2402440)[33].

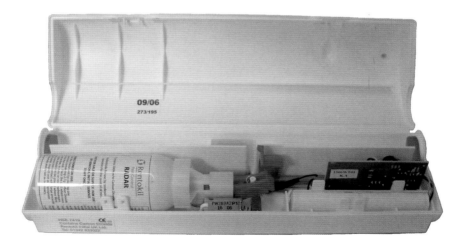

Fig. 58 *Radar* mouse trap

Traps of Unkown Manufacturers

In the case of a trap, where its construction suggests a particular maker, I have placed the trap with that maker. For example I have put **Ikat-chem** and **Victory** with Procter Brothers. Those traps, for which I have absolutely no clue as to the maker, I have assembled in this final chapter. Again they are in probable chronological order and in the absence of known manufacturers I have used the names of the traps as headings.

Fig. 59 *Chute* mouse trap

Chute
This trap is only known from a single advertisement (Fig. 59) in the 1907 Catalogue of the H.A.Goodall & Co., Ltd of London & Paris. It was patented in August 1899 (GB12128) by Frank Lumley, Ironmonger, of Brixton, London. No examples seem to have survived.

Safe Setter
This small gin trap (Figs 60a and b), evidently specially designed for the capture of birds or mice, was advertised (Fig. 60c) in the 1908 Catalogue of Crowden & Garrod Ltd, Hardware Merchants of London.

Fig. 60a

set

Fig. 60b

GIN BIRD OR MOUSE TRAP.

set

The "Safe Setter." Bright Steel.
3 doz. in a box, 3/ per doz.

Fig. 60c

Fig. 60 *Safe Setter* mouse trap

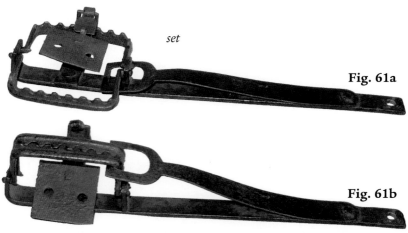

set

Fig. 61a

Fig. 61b

MOUSE OR SMALL BIRD TRAP.

Fig. 61c

Bird or Mouse Traps.

FLAT OR BOW SPRINGS.

set

Fig. 61d

Fig. 61 Bird or Mouse *Gin* traps

Gin

Small gin traps of normal design with roughly two inch jaws and either a flat (Figs 61a and b) or bowed spring were made for the capture of mice or small birds, but unlike many larger gin traps, they rarely seem to bear the name or mark of the maker. They were advertised in the catalogues of H.Lane (1908-13) and W.& G. Sidebotham (pre 1915) (Figs 61c and d) and were no doubt also made by many of the other trap makers of Wednesfield, Staffordshire[34].

set

Fig. 62 *Catch* mouse trap

Catch

The **Catch** mouse trap was patented by Hanbury Dunnett of Knowle and Edwin Waring of Leamington, Warwickshire in 1908 (GB14367 and 21294). It was advertised (Fig. 62) in a Catalogue (date unknown) of Milbro of London. No surviving examples are known.

Safety First

The **Safety First** mouse trap was patented by Yelverton Corrie of Victoria, London in 1924 (GB237424). It was advertised (Fig. 63) in the 1931-32 Catalogue of the Army & Navy Stores of Victoria, London. No surviving examples are known.

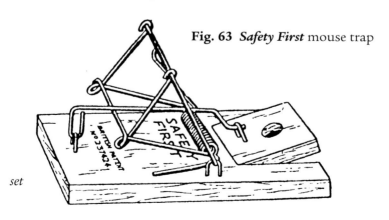

Fig. 63 *Safety First* mouse trap

set

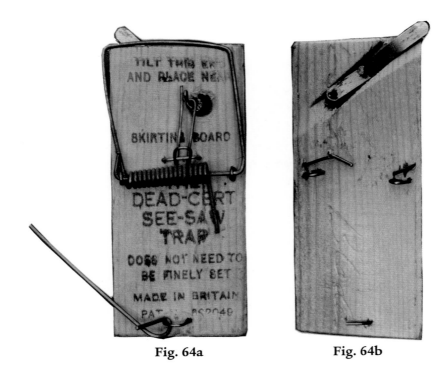

Fig. 64a   Fig. 64b

Fig. 64 *Dead-Cert See-Saw* mouse trap

Dead-Cert See-Saw

The **Dead-Cert See-Saw** mouse trap (Figs 64a and b) was designed by Henry Altham of Wrexham, Denbighshire. He applied for a patent in October 1945 and it was accepted in May 1948 (GB602049). He also applied for a US patent in August 1947 that was confirmed in May 1952 (US2598205). No advertisements are known.

Recent Traps of Overseas Origin

Before embarking on this final chapter it is worth pointing out that of some ninety traps so far described and illustrated several have already been identified as having been influenced at least to some extent by designers in continental Europe and North America. In the last few decades however this overseas influence has markedly increased and today it is American trap designers that have taken centre stage. Indeed of the large number of mouse traps currently available in Britain, well over half the designs have originated in America. For the British market they have often been modified, renamed and repackaged by a number of different companies. To explore and attempt to unravel this ever changing and somewhat complex situation as it stands at the time of writing (October, 2007), I will simply list in alphabetical order the original overseas names of the traps and follow their subsequent moves. Their current distribution throughout Britain in retail stores such as iron-mongers and garden centres seems to be very patchy, but many are readily available on the internet through a number of agents.

Better

The ***Better*** mouse trap (Fig. 65a) with its unusual spring was invent-ed by Walter Schildt of Brooklyn Center, Minnesota, and patented by him in 1991 (US 4991340). It was made and distributed in America by Intruder Inc. of Rice Lake, Wisconsin. Subsequently various versions of this trap have appeared for sale in Britain. One named the ***Safe N' Sure*** (Fig. 65b) made by the Roundpoint Peg Co. of Victoria, Australia, was available from Coopers of Bishop Stortford, Herts. Another plastic version is available in black from rolson quality tools of Twyford, Berkshire and in bright orange from Jobdone, Peerslade Ltd of Brentwood, Essex (Figs 65c and d). Yet another has been produced by STV International of Little Cressington, Norfolk, and marked with its Trade Mark "The Big Cheese" (Fig. 65e).

Fig. 65 *Better* mouse trap and its progeny

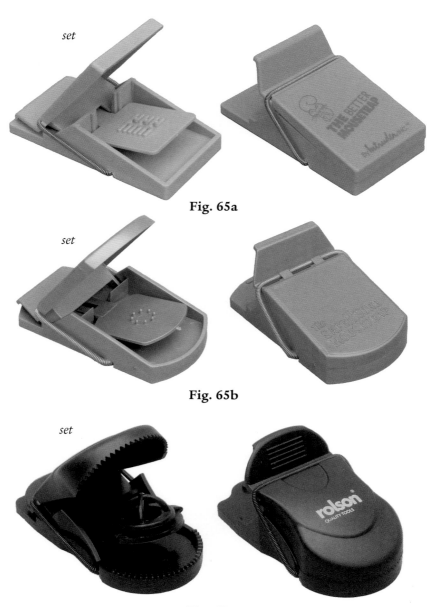

set

Fig. 65a

set

Fig. 65b

set

Fig. 65c

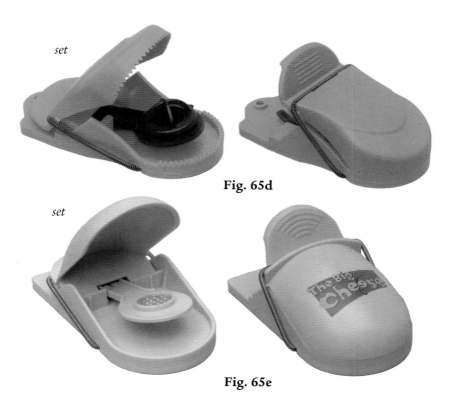

set

Fig. 65d

set

Fig. 65e

Cant Miss Four-way

This wooden snap trap was designed by Herbert Stilson of Chicago, Illinois and patented (US 2103877) by him in 1937[35] (Fig. 66a). It was made for very many years by the McGill Metal Products Company of Marengo, Illinois, until Woodstream acquired McGill's trap-making Division in the 1990s and closed down all of its trap production. Many other companies have subsequently recognised the value of Stilson's design and made it available again. All such traps, apart from the name or design printed on them, look identical in construction and are probably all made by the same manufacturer in Taiwan. In Britain STV International market one displaying its "The Big Cheese" Trade Mark and the Procter Bros Pest-Stop *Wooden* Mouse Trap is marked with a white mouse against a red circular background (Figs 66b and c).

Fig. 66a

Fig. 66b

Fig. 66c

Fig. 66 *Cant Miss Four-way* and copies

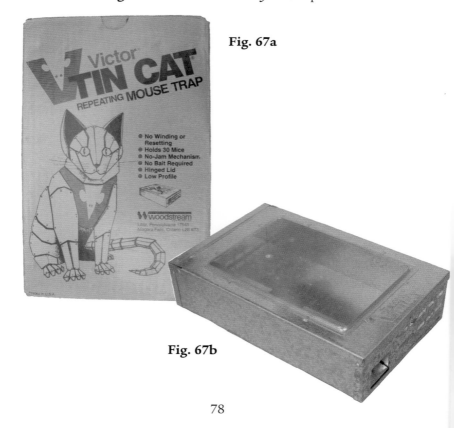

Fig. 67a

Fig. 67b

Delusion

The multi-catch Delusion mouse trap was invented by John Morris of Seward, Nebraska, and patented (US 195,632) by him in 1877[36]. Its particular innovation of a see-saw that flips up a door that prevents a caught mouse from escaping is still in use to-day, especially in Woodstream's large metal Victor *Tin Cat* (Figs 67a and b) and its smaller plastic version labelled Victor *Poison-Free* (Fig. 67c). The Procter Bros versions of these two traps are respectively the Pest Stop *Multi-Mouse* trap and the Pest Stop *Multi-Catch* mouse trap (Fig. 67d). Those of STV are The Big Cheese *Multi-Mouse* and The Big Cheese *Multi-Catch* (Fig. 67e).

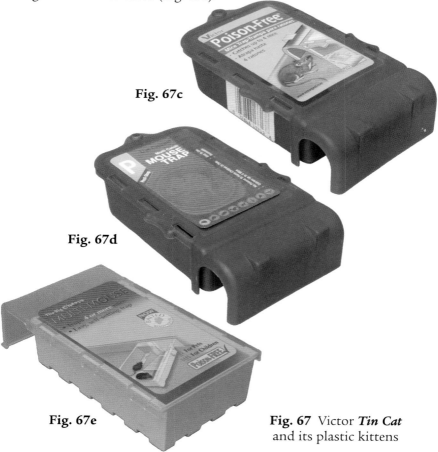

Fig. 67c

Fig. 67d

Fig. 67e

Fig. 67 Victor *Tin Cat* and its plastic kittens

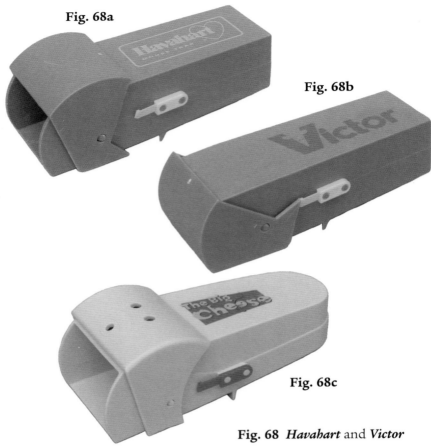

Fig. 68a

Fig. 68b

Fig. 68c

Fig. 68 *Havahart* and *Victor*

Havahart

This plastic tilting single-catch live mouse trap (Fig. 68a) was invented by Robert Spiller of Laguna Hills, California, and patented (US 4550523) in 1985. Its manufacturer in the USA is Woodstream of Lititz, Pennsylvania, who soon changed its name to **Victor** (Fig. 68b), presumably to avoid confusion with a completely different series of all-metal Havahart traps[37] for a variety of animals already being made by the same company. A modified version of the **Victor** live-catch mouse trap is now being made and marketed by STV International of Little Cressington, Norfolk, and marked with its Trade Mark "The Big Cheese" (Fig. 68c).

Ketch-All

This large metal wind-up mouse trap (Fig. 69a) was designed by Austin Kness of Audubon, Iowa and patented by him in 1930 (US 1758952) with further modifications patented by him (US 2433913) in 1948 following his move to Albia, Iowa, where it is still being made by the Kness Manufacturing Company[38]. A copy of one of its later versions is being made in China and is marketed in Britain by Procter Bros as the Pest Stop *Automatic* Mouse Trap (Fig. 69b).

Fig. 69a

Fig. 69c

Fig. 69 *Ketch-All* wind-up mouse trap (a) and copy (b)

81

Ketch-All II

This plastic snap trap with its separate metal setting and striking frames was designed by Lester, Marvin and Arnold Kness of Albia, Iowa and patented by them in 1981 (US 4297805) and 1983 (US4369595). Lester Kness patented further modifications in 1987 (US 4711049). The trap (Figs 70a-c) is made by Kness Manufacturing Co. of Albia, Iowa, who now market it packaged as the *Snap-E* mouse trap although the plastic base itself may still bear the imprint of the earlier name *Ketch-All II*.

Modifications available in Britain include a green plastic one named *Easy-Set* (Fig. 70d) marketed by Growing Success Organics Ltd of Zeals, Wiltshire, bearing the company's bee logo. A white plastic one (Fig. 70e) is marked SIL PLC, while a red and black version named *Sure-Set* (Fig. 70f) is available from Procter Bros. This last is made in China and has US Patent Pending embossed beneath the base.

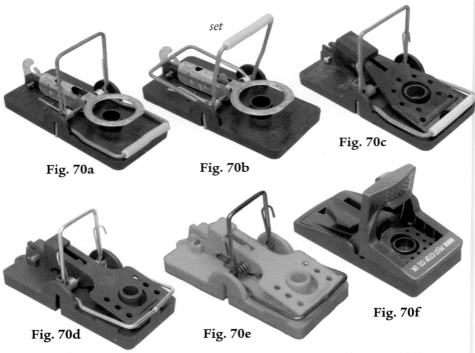

Fig. 70a

Fig. 70b

Fig. 70c

Fig. 70d

Fig. 70e

Fig. 70f

Fig. 70 *Ketch-All II/Snap-E* mouse traps (a-c) and copies (d-f)

Fig. 71a

Fig. 71b

Fig. 71c

Fig. 71 *Mice Cube*
mouse traps

Mice Cube

This simple single-catch mouse trap of clear plastic with a push-up door was patented in 1988 (US 4,787,170) by William Kingsbury and Kenneth Bernard of Haverhill, Massachusetts. It is manufactured in the USA by Pied Piper International Inc. of Plaistow, New Hampshire (Figs 71a and b) and distributed in Britain as the ***FITO Humane*** (Fig. 71c) mouse trap by LC Solutions of Milton Keynes.

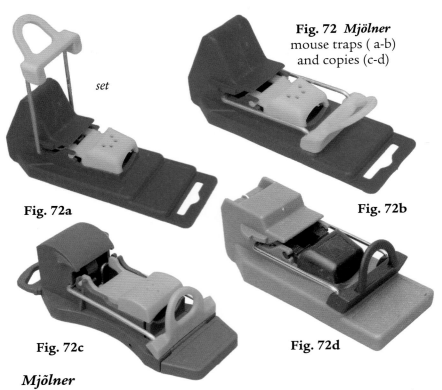

set

Fig. 72 *Mjölner*
mouse traps (a-b)
and copies (c-d)

Fig. 72a

Fig. 72b

Fig. 72c

Fig. 72d

Mjölner

This Swedish mouse trap named after Thor's hammer was patented in Sweden by its inventor Göran Hansson in 1995 and subsequently elsewhere including the USA in 1999 (US 5960593). The *Mjölner* (Figs 72a and b) continues to be made in Sweden by GH Trap Teknik AB, but a further authorised version is being made in China and distributed in the USA by Woodstream who have named it the Victor *Quick Kill*. This version is now marketed in Britain by Procter Bros as the Pest-Stop *Quick Kill* Advanced (Fig. 72d) The important innovative feature of the *Mjölner* and the *Quick Kill* is that a mouse has to raise the cover of the bait container only slightly to release an exceptionally swift and strong striker.

Another version of the *Mjölner* made in Sweden by Vangus AB and marketed as *exMus* (Fig. 72c) has since been withdrawn, since it was unauthorised and infringed the original patent. This version was marketed briefly in the UK by STV International as the Big Cheese *Gotcha*.

Mouse Glue

Packs of ready-to-use card or plastic rectangles smeared with glue for the control of mice have been available in the USA from many manufacturers for many years. They have appeared in Britain from time to time but do not appear to have found much favour. At present they only seem to be available here from STV International who market them as Big Cheese *Mouse Glue* traps.

Safeset

This unusual white plastic snap trap was designed by Lubomir and Helena Vajs of Toronto, Canada, and patented by them in 1987 (US 4665644) and again in 1989 (US 4803799). It is made in Canada by the H.L. International Marketing Corporation of Scarborough, Ontario, Canada. The name *Safeset* is embossed on each trap but it is marketed and packaged in many countries under a variety of names. In Britain it is available from Procter Bros who for a time labelled it *Little Nipper* (Fig. 73a), giving it the same name as its British-made wooden snap trap, but now packages it as Pest Stop *Snap Trap*.

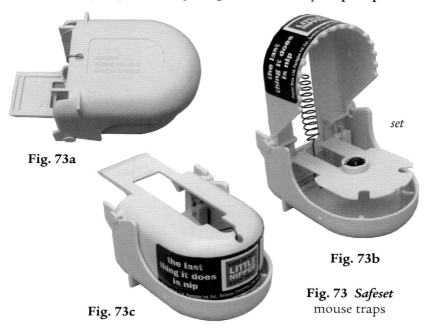

Fig. 73a

set

Fig. 73b

Fig. 73c

Fig. 73 *Safeset*
mouse traps

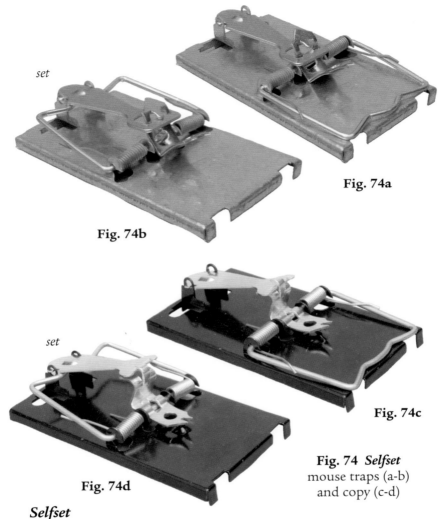

set

Fig. 74a

Fig. 74b

set

Fig. 74c

Fig. 74d

Fig. 74 *Selfset*
mouse traps (a-b)
and copy (c-d)

Selfset

The British designed all-metal *Selfset* mouse trap (Figs 23 and 74a) has been copied and redesigned in China. This Chinese manufactured trap is now available from Procter Bros as its Pest Stop *Easy Setting* Metal Mouse Trap (Fig. 74b). Its design is identical to that of the *Selfset* except that the set/release mechanism has been modified so that the striker is released when the bait hook is depressed. The base is lacquered black.

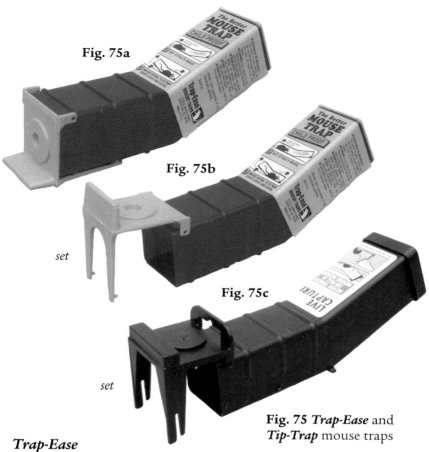

Fig. 75a

Fig. 75b

set

Fig. 75c

set

Fig. 75 *Trap-Ease* and *Tip-Trap* mouse traps

Trap-Ease

This plastic live trap (Figs 75a and b) was invented by Melvin Melton of San Clemente, California, to whom a patent was granted in 1986 (US 4578892) and a company was established for its manufacture, Trap-Ease Inc of Santa Ana, California. The company was subsequently acquired (c.2000) by the Kness Mfg Co. of Albia, Iowa, who made minor modifications and renamed the trap as *Tip-Trap*. This is the trap that is now being marketed in Britain by Rentokil Initial and labelled the *Rentokil Live Capture* (Fig.75c), though the name *Tip-Trap* remains embossed on the end of the trap. It is also available as the *Easy-Set* Live Mouse Catcher from Growing Success Organics Ltd of Zeals, Wiltshire.

Fig. 76 Victor *Electronic*
mouse traps

Electronic

The Victor **Electronic** mouse trap was patented by David Swift of Lititz, PA and Christopher Rich of Lancaster, PA on August 26, 2003 (US6609328). They assigned the patent to the Woodstream Corp. of Lititz, PA. The black plastic trap (Fig. 76) is made in China and requires 4 AA batteries to provide sufficient power to electrocute a mouse. It is marketed in Britain as the **Electronic Mouse Killer** by Procter Bros.

Wire Cage

There is a long tradition of wire cage traps being used in continental Europe, where they continue to be made both as dome-shaped multi-catch traps and single-catch rectangular cages (Figs 77a and b). Such traps are occasionally marketed in Britain and may have been specially produced for that purpose, like the single-catch **Catchalive** (Fig. 77c) marketed by Bakaware Limited of Birmingham.

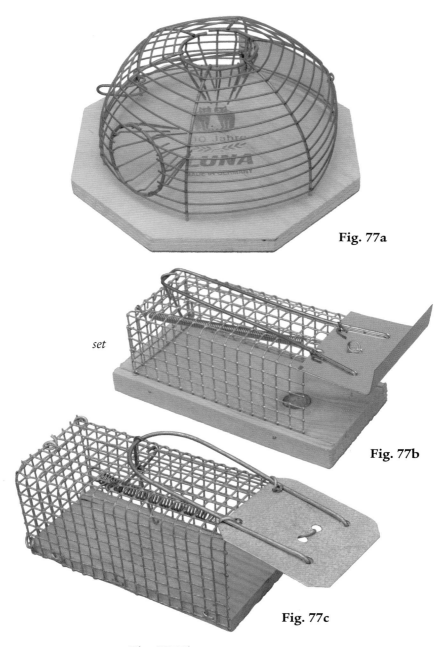

set

Fig. 77a

Fig. 77b

Fig. 77c

Fig. 77 Wire cage mouse traps

ACKNOWLEDGMENTS

This book could not have been written without a great deal of help from various people and organisations that not only provided me with information, but permitted me to photograph the traps within their care. For all their help I am indebted to The Museum of English Rural Life, The Shaftsbury Museum, John Bailey, Trevor Bateman, Norman Brazell, Roy Brigden, Andy Brigham, George Clarke, Chuck Clift, Fred Courtier, Stuart Haddon-Riddoch, Maurice Juggins, Bob Kwalwasser, Simon Levesley, Adrian Meyer, Jeremy Procter, Ken Rattee and Ricky Seiter.

REFERENCES AND NOTES

1   David Drummond (2005) *Mouse traps: A Quick Scamper through their Long History.* North American Trap Collectors Association, Galloway, Ohio.

2   Leonard Mascall (1590) *A Booke of Engines and traps to take Polcats, Buzardes, Rattes, Mice and all other kindes of Vermine and beasts whatsoever, most profitable for all Warriners, and such as delight in this kinde of sport and pastime.* Printed in London by John Wolfe. A facsimile edition was published in 1973 by Theatrum Orbis Terrarum Ltd, Amsterdam & De Capo Press Inc. New York.

3   David Drummond (1992) Unmasking Mascall's Mouse Traps. *Proceedings of the 15th Vertebrate Pest Conference.* University of California.

4   James Hornell (1940) Old English Dead-fall Traps. *Antiquity* **14**(56).

5   The addresses of these Birmingham mouse trap maker's are revealed by Stuart Haddon-Riddoch (2006) *Rural Reflections* Argyll Publishing, Argyll, pp 228, 232 and 249.

6   David Drummond (1994) Colin Pullinger and his Perpetual Mouse Trap. *Sussex Industrial History* **24**, 2-9.

7   David Drummond (2004) Colin Pullinger's Registered Designs. *Sussex Industrial History* **34**, 36-37.

8   Jarrolds Directory.

9   White's Suffolk Directory.

10 Kelly's Directory.

11 The Leggett and Company Catalogue, purchased quite by chance from an Ephemera Dealer, is currently in the possession of the author. It was printed by A.M.Sparks of Ipswich and includes, apart from 17 mouse traps, three rat traps, a beetle trap, a plate rack, a portable meat safe and hardwood and deal soap boxes.

12 Hardware Companies advertising in their catalogues mouse traps comparable to those made by Leggett & Co. include G. Harding & Sons of London (1891, 1901 and 1902), Joseph Nichols & Son of Birmingham (1880s and 1898-1900) and H.A.Goodall & Co. of London (1907).

13 David Drummond (1997) Irish Mouse Traps. *Folk Life* **35**, 54-62.

14 David Drummond (1996) The Johnstone Mouse Trap Factory. *Scottish Industrial History* **18**, 52-67.

15 The "Little Nipper" Mouse-trap formed the subject of a short illustrated note in *The Ironmonger* of Jan14, 1899 p.53.

16 Lincoln Bros of 60/62 Vyner Street, London, E2 advertised their **Victory** mouse trap on page 853 of *Benn's Encyclopedia*, 1956

17 This item of information was obtained during a phone conversation the author had with the widow of Richard Evans in February 1993. Evans had died in September of the previous year.

18 Stuart Haddon-Riddoch (2006) *Rural Reflections. A Brief History of Traps, Trapmakers and Gamekeepers in Britain*. Revised and enlarged Edition, pp187-189.

19 David Drummond (2002) Carl Bender and his Automatic Self-setting "Capito" Mouse Trap. *Hessische Blätter für Volks- und Kulturforschung* **37/38**, 99-116.

20 Mark Hovell's book "Rats and how to destroy them" published in 1924 by Bale & Danielsson Ltd contains a full page advertisement for Winstone's **Ratsticker** and also advertises the Rat-catching Varnish of Dane & Co. and the Kay Brothers' Dak Ratlime.

21 A substantial collection of Army & Navy Catalogues are housed in the Archives and Business Record Centre of The University of Glasgow.

22 James Ritchie (1931) *Beasts and Birds as Farm Pests*. Oliver & Boyd, Edinburgh & London. p.67.

23 The best information about S. Young & Son (Misterton) Ltd is undoubtedly to be found in pages 252-266 of Stuart Haddon-Riddoch's *Rural Reflections* – see ref. 18.

24 Stuart Haddon-Riddoch (2006) *Rural Reflections.* pp 209-211.

25 Robert A. Matthews (1941 and 1942) *Details of a simple device to help battery set owners to operate their receivers without high tension batteries.* (1942) *Details of a simple and super efficient device to help battery set owners to operate their receivers without high tension batteries. Incorporating an atom-disintegrating automatic arc.*

26 Robert A. Jollife (1944) *The Seven Year Cycle. The solution to an astronomical problem after 15 years study and experiment.* This pamphlet and the two others are available in the British Library.

27 Dennis Chitty & D.A.Kempson (1949) Prebaiting Small Mammals and a new design of live trap. *Ecology* **30**(4) 536-542.

28 J.Gurnell & J.R.Flowerdew (2006) *Live Trapping Small Mammals. A Practical Guide 4th Edition.* The Mammal Society, 2B Inworth Street, London, SW11 3EP.

29 R.A.Davis (1961) A simple live-trap for small mammals. *Proc. Zool. Soc. London* **137**, 631-633.

30 Anon (1973) Rounding up those rodents. *Cage Birds and Aviary* 3 May, 1973 p.10. Correspondence from R.T.Clements "Those traps!" in *Gamekeeper and Countryside* September, 1979 p.390, and from J.A.Ratcliffe "Mousetrap Inventor" in the same journal of October, 1979 p.35.

31 Prufrock (1972) TASS the Mouse Killer. *Sunday Times* 24 September, 1972, pp53 and 65.

32 Modern mousetrap meets food industry standards. *Pest Control* March 2003 **63**, 43.

33 More details of Rentokil's **Radar** are available in Rentokil Pest Control R&D Technical Release 157.

34 Stuart Haddon-Riddoch (2006) *Rural Reflections* Chapter 3.

35 David Drummond (2006) *McGill Mouse Traps and the Stilson Brothers.* North American Trap Collectors Association, Galloway, Ohio.

36 David Drummond (1997) The Delusion of John Morris. *Nebraska History* **78**, 64-74.

37 David Drummond (2004) Better Mouse Traps: the history of their development in the USA. *Proc. 10th Wildlife Damage Management Conference* (2004):388-397.

38 Gooch, H. (1999) Kness celebrates 75 years. *Pest Control* **67(5)**, 90-92.

FURTHER READING

For those readers interested in a wider range of British Mammal Traps and the background to their use the following books are recommended:-

John Bailey (2007) *British Traps for Mammals. More than 500 British Mammal Traps Classified, Illustrated and Described*. Fieldfare Publishing. Many excellent drawings of traps, including mouse traps, by the author.

James Bateman (1988) *Animal Traps and Trapping*. Revised Edition. David & Charles.

Stuart Haddon-Riddoch (2006) *Rural Reflections. A Brief History of Traps, Trapmakers and Gamekeeping in Britain*. Second Edition. Argyll Publishing.

Roger Lovegrove (2007) *Silent Fields. The long decline of a nation's wildlife*. Oxford University Press. A detailed history of the way that trapping and other related activities have affected British birds and mammals.

INDEXES

Traps

Designers and Manufacturers